THE CONTRIBUTIONS OF
HARRY STACK SULLIVAN

The Contributions of Harry Stack Sullivan

A SYMPOSIUM ON INTERPERSONAL THEORY IN
PSYCHIATRY AND SOCIAL SCIENCE

Edited by PATRICK MULLAHY

SCIENCE HOUSE, New York

The quotations and excerpts from Dr. Harry Stack Sullivan's unpublished works and unpublished lectures which are included in this volume with the kind permission of the William Alanson White Psychiatric Foundation, 1711 Rhode Island Avenue, N. W., Washington, D. C., may not be republished, except in conjunction with book reviews, without permission of the Foundation.

Many of these quotations and excerpts are taken from transcriptions of recordings of Dr. Sullivan's lectures and "talks," often delivered informally, and may contain some minor inaccuracies.

Manufactured in the United States of America

INTRODUCTION

Since 1952, when *The Contributions* was published, several series of Sullivan's lectures have appeared. Psychiatrists and psychologists now have a more adequate basis for knowing and evaluating his achievements. Yet a great many misunderstandings of Sullivan's ideas still exist. One hopes that these lectures, which are relatively non-technical and contain concise explications of most of his important conceptions, will clarify some of these misunderstandings and contribute toward a more profound grasp of interpersonal theory.

Sullivan conceived of psychiatry in two senses: one, in which he adhered to the traditional notion of psychiatry as the study and treatment of those suffering mental disorder, whether mild or severe, a view which he at one time labeled psychopathology; a second, in which he conceived of psychiatry as a discipline closely approximating social psychology, that is, as a science of interpersonal relations. In this sense, psychiatry has very broad limits, which cannot be specified rigorously, since its subject matter does not fit into neat categories. Not surprisingly, some people who are used to rather fixed divisions, departments, and classifications have little use for this orientation. Nevertheless, Sullivan thought that this broader orientation is necessary if psychiatry is ever to realize its rich potential for human betterment.

The most concise summary of Sullivan's contributions has been written by Sullivan himself. Very early in his career—roughly around 1930—he had formulated what for its time was a spectacularly brilliant and relatively comprehensive psychiatric theory and, along with it, a powerful elaboration of Freud's psychoanalytic method. Already he had begun to commit those ideas to paper in a relatively systematic fashion. The manuscript was completed, though not, perhaps, to Sullivan's satisfaction, around 1932 or 1933. Since he did not publish it, it lay around for a whole generation unread by and unknown to all but a few people such as Harold Lagswell, John Dollard, Clara Thompson and myself. Finally, in 1965, it was copyrighted by the William Alanson White Psychiatric Foundation, Inc., Washington, D.C., under the title of *Personal Psychopathology*. While it is an early, tentative formulation of interpersonal psychiatry, and although it contains some ideas that are of dubious validity, it is nevertheless, I think, a powerful and original work.

On page one and two of that work he says:

"As we are all much more simply human than otherwise, so psychopathology deals chiefly with matters of common experience, but with matters the *personal significance* of which is in each case veiled from the person concerned in each unfortunate complex of social living. It does not deal with diseases in the sense of medical entities like scarlet fever, but instead with processes of living that are unusually inefficient, productive of strain and unhappiness, and contributory to failures of the individual as a self-respecting unit. . . ."

There exist "numbers of our contemporaries in the case of whom the maintenance of some measure of self-respect is a never-ending task, and one entailing great cost not only in personal effort but also in interferences with the comfort and success of others. It may be said that whenever the maintenance of self-esteem becomes an end instead of a consequent of life, the individual concerned is mentally sick and a subject for psychopathological study, finally to be understood by the same formulae that we must work out for understanding the 'neurotic' and the 'insane.'"

PATRICK MULLAHY

January, 1967

CONTENTS

ACKNOWLEDGMENT

In preparing this volume for publication, Mrs. Lloyd Merrill and Mrs. Bernice Platt of the staff of the William Alanson White Institute were of considerable assistance. It is a pleasure to acknowledge their efficient aid.

THE EDITOR

SULLIVAN'S CONCEPTIONS

CHAPTER I

THE THEORIES
OF H. S. SULLIVAN

PATRICK MULLAHY

*Formerly Columbia University and
the William Alanson White Institute*

MANY years ago William James made the observation that a theory often runs through three stages in its career. First it is attacked as absurd. Then, in its second stage, it is admitted to be true but obvious and insignificant. And in its final stage it is considered to be so important that its adversaries claim that they discovered it themselves. I believe interpersonal theory is now in the third stage.

While I do not intend to deal at any length with objections to or criticisms of the theory, I want to take notice of one criticism, which is of the very term itself. Some people have said that the term "interpersonal" is only a more elaborate and more pretentious way of expressing what the word "personal" has always conveyed. Now such an objection overlooks the fact that a word, a term in discourse, has its meaning fixed primarily according to what social usage ordains whether the usage be confined to a small group, or to a whole continent. This does not deny the well-known fact that a term may have several meanings or a private penumbra of meaning, in the psychological sense of meaning. In any case, the term interpersonal does *not* have the meaning in Sullivan's theories and in the usage of some of his students which the term "personal" has had traditionally. I might almost say that this paper will be devoted to showing how and why.

I shall discuss interpersonal theory first and very briefly from the philosophical side in an attempt to clarify some of the things which make an understanding of the theory or theories more difficult. We are still struggling with at least two influential conceptions which are a hindrance to our understanding of psychiatry as a study of interpersonal relations. The first pertains to the notion that man has a dual nature. The second has to do with the idea that man is a more or less self-contained entity, an idea which springs primarily from atomistic individualistic conceptions of man. I refer here to the kind of thinking which treats individualism as if it were a static thing, having "uniform content," which "ignores the fact that the mental and moral structure of individuals, the pattern of their desires and purposes, change with every great change in social institutions." [1]

According to the first conception, the dual nature of man is manifested in a material, physical, bodily part, and a spiritual or mental part. In one dualistic conception, man is conceived of as primarily and essentially a soul temporarily lodged in a body. Another dualistic idea conceives of man in terms of mind and body. In either of the two dualistic approaches man is a twofold being whose soul or mind is essentially distinct from the bodily make-up. This dualism persists in popular thinking.

Adolf Meyer was, I believe, the first psychiatrist in America to get rid of this dualism while abandoning the crude mechanism prevalent in psychiatry about a half a cenutry ago. In any case, he conceived personality in functional terms, and in an environmental setting.[2] According to Sullivan's statement, Meyer "denied the usefulness of preoccupation with neural analogies. He indi-

[1] *Intelligence in the Modern World, John Dewey's Philosophy.* Edited, with an introduction, by Joseph Ratner, The Modern Library, New York, p. 410. Compare F. H. Bradley's essay "My Station and Its Duties" in *Ethical Studies (Selected Essays)* with an introduction by Ralph G. Ross, the Liberal Arts Press, New York, 1951.

[2] *The Common Sense Psychiatry of Adolf Meyer.* Edited with Biographical Narrative by Alfred Lief, McGraw-Hill Book Co., Inc., New York, 1948.

cated that it is by a superordination of physiology by means of the integrating functions and particularly by means of the use of symbols as tools that man was able to develop, on the one hand, his remarkable problems in dealing with his personal reality and the reality of others around him." [3] Perhaps when I come to try to communicate Sullivan's ideas about symbols you will see some of Meyer's influence.

Among his many achievements, Freud revealed the experiential origin of specific limitations of personal awareness, and of many personality difficulties, as well as discovering a powerful new therapeutic technique. Nevertheless he was seriously handicapped by individualistic notions of man inherited from the nineteenth century or earlier.

In regard to the achievements of William Alanson White, Dr. Winfred Overholser, Superintendent of Saint Elizabeth's Hospital in Washington, D. C., has been good enough to call my attention to the following:

> "He [Dr. White] was an able executive and administrator," Dr. Overholser observes, "but I have long had the feeling that his significant contributions to psychiatry have not been fully appreciated. He was, of course, one of the very early advocates of the Freudian psychoanalysis but one reason for that was that he, himself, had done a very considerable amount of work on the unconscious with Dr. Boris Sidis. In addition he made an intelligible and readily understandable presentation of the concepts both of Freud and of Meyer. To my mind, he had a broader point of view and was more synthetic than either Freud or Meyer." [4]

According to Sullivan, White envisioned the first synthesis of the two great trends in psychiatry, the medical and "the other great body of observational techniques, formulations, hypotheses

[3] *Conceptions of Modern Psychiatry* by Harry Stack Sullivan, William A. White Psychiatric Foundation, Washington, D. C., 1947, p. 4.

[4] Personal communication.

and experiments which are included in all those efforts to understand social situations and to deal with social problems as they have appeared in the history of man." [5]

The next step, he goes on to say, "came with the realization that the field of psychiatry is neither the mentally sick individual nor the successful and unsuccessful processes that may be observed in groups and that can be studied in detached objectivity. Psychiatry, instead, is the study of processes that involve or go on between people. The field of psychiatry is the field of interpersonal relations, under any and all circumstances in which these relations exist. It was seen that a *personality* can never be isolated from the complex of interpersonal relations in which the person lives and has his being." [6]

In the early days, the evolution of interpersonal theory seems to have been aided by, among others, the anthropologist Sapir, the philosopher Mead and the sociologists Thomas and Cooley.

It sometimes seems that old ideas never die. Remnants of the conception of the dual nature of man persist as exemplified in such phrases as "psychosomatic medicine." Some books on psychiatry discuss what their authors call intrapsychic processes. Such a notion in effect retains the conception of a soul, though shorn of certain qualities and religious associations, and translated into Greek. Now as long as we retain the notion of an inner psyche, the theory or theories of interpersonal relations will sound puzzling, strange, if not incomprehensible or perverse. We have to drag this inner psyche out-of-doors and give it an airing.

I want to stress, then, that at least remnants of the traditional conception of man as a twofold being persist in psychiatric thinking, as manifested in such phrases as psychosomatic medicine, intrapsychic processes, and in other ways. According to some people it would appear also that whatever makes us a human being, whatever constitutes human personality, is thought to reside within us, cooped up in a tower in our own private castle. We look within, as the phrase goes, to discover, who am I, and

[5] Sullivan, op. cit., p. 4.

[6] Op. cit., pp. 4-5.

what am I? And obviously this has at least a seeming plausibility for we do carry on what is ordinarily labeled introspection, and we do seem to organize our experiences around an ego, an "I" which is usually the center of conscious reference.

What is not ordinarily realized is that the meaning of our so-called inner experiences are not revealed primarily by a direct inspection or by intuition but by inference even though often swift so that in a moment we seem to traverse a whole inferential chain. Second, we do not always know that our experiences centered around "I" represent only a part of our personality. Again we often fail to realize that our self, a part of that to which we refer when we say "I," and our entire personality, have developed from an interpersonal history. Nor do we always see that our inner covert experiences have either direct or indirect symbolic reference to others. Finally, we often do not understand that our inner experience has been built up from select excerpts assimilated from the cultural heritage, that our personality is a creative expression of the culture or sub-culture in which we have our being.[7]

The notion that personality embodies a spiritual essence or a psyche, encapsulated within us, is so deeply engrained, even though slightly disguised in a different language, that when one speaks of interpersonal relations we tend to think in terms of two fixed and static entities, two self-contained minds or personalities temporarily "doing business," carrying on some kind of action with each other which leaves them essentially unchanged. Any suggestion that the person is not as self-sustaining, as self-enclosed, and as self-contained as might appear seems to threaten us with a denial of our individuality or to plunge personality or human nature into a chaos of absolute relativism.

In other words, while we may recognize and identify a man or a person as a particularity, as a "numerical unit," who initiates activity, we cannot *understand* him thus. We can understand him only when we take account of his manifold aspects and rela-

---

[7] According to one of Sullivan's formulations, the "envelope" or containing manifold of personality is the totality of roles which are learned in interpersonal relations, their analysis, and resynthesis into "original" patterns.

tions—physical, biological, socio-cultural. When I say that the person initiates activity, I do not mean that man has metaphysical free will which while not governed by natural laws can initiate activity. Nor do I mean that the person is in any way uncontrolled by or divorced from natural conditions.

While I cannot take time to enter into a discussion of will, a conception which Sullivan was very hostile to for understandable reasons—patients do so much talking about using their will power—I think that many people, including Harry Stack Sullivan, are philosophically unclear on this issue, for he consistently equates will and free will with metaphysical entities.[8]

Sullivan was opposed to the notion of individuality as a useful conception for psychiatry and, as in the case of the problem of will, with some justification. But he identified individuality with the uniquely private and thereby set up a straw man, which he could demolish with great gusto in his lectures.[9]

For him, however, personality is essentially a creative expression or embodiment of socio-cultural processes. And anyone who will take the trouble to scan some of the literature of anthropology and sociology with an unbiased mind will, I think, find this idea magnificently corroborated.

Certain controversies have arisen concerning the definition of "person" and "personality." But leaving aside such controversies, let us see how Sullivan conceived of personality. For him personality is relegated to the realm of hypothetical entities. It is the hypothetical entity postulated to account for the dynamic character of interpersonal relations. Personal individuality he regarded as entirely irrelevant to psychiatry as the study of interpersonal relations.

There are two classes of people or persons, the one overt, "real," the other "imaginary," or eidetic. Interpersonal relations involve not only real, actual people but also covert, "imaginary,"

[8] Compare, "Will, Choice and Ends" by Patrick Mullahy, *Psychiatry*, Vol. 12, No. 4, November, 1949.

[9] *Conceptions of Modern Psychiatry*, p. vi, and "The Illusion of Unique Individuality" *Psychiatry*, Vol. 13, No. 3, August, 1950.

or "eidetic" persons. In speaking of a person, we refer to someone actually extant, or "imaginary" or a "blend" of both.

So interpersonal theory includes much more than what occurs
between two or more living people present in a given situation.
For example, we develop supervisory patterns of the self, which
are sub-organizations of the self-system, which come into being
for the maintenance of self-esteem and the esteem of others as
a result of past interpersonal relations and experiences. These
internal supervisory patterns are manifested, for instance, as the
internal auditor which one organizes more or less unwittingly to
hear what one says, the reader of what one writes, and the watch-
ful spectator for the way one behaves. These supervisory patterns
of the self or "internal critics" have both a constructive and often
a destructive function.[10]

Eidetic ("imaginary") "people" are not confined to personifications which have some direct historical relation to those who
exerted a supervisory or critical role in the past. A person may,
in reverie, create "imaginary people" who, for example, like him
or dislike him, and to whom in fantasy he reacts with like or
dislike. These abstract personifications of course do have a relation to the significant others in his past life and very likely to
those who are significant to him in the present and foreseeable
future. I cannot take space to touch on the various complications
which relate to fantasy, psychotic productions, "projections" and
the like. Summarily, we all develop symbol processes and personifications, which represent the enduring manifestations of past
experience in interpersonal relations.

These covert "people," which are known by inference only,
are what Sullivan called eidetic people. All that is covert is said
to arise from what was once overt, that is, has a "necessary relationship" to something which has been overt. The more difficult
aspect of interpersonal theory, Sullivan observed, "requires attention to the surviving influence and foresightful impact of un-

---

[10] Charles H. Cooley's *Human Nature and the Social Order* (1902) contains a beautiful discussion of "eidetic" people, though he lacks Sullivan's
dynamic approach.

embodied but none the less characterizable personified existents, these eidetic people historically related to 'real' people of one's past experience, but related to them in a dynamic rather than a mere static survival way. I mean here that eidetic people, these potent personifications, change, however slowly; they too are altered by experience subsequent to the occasions on which their particular prototypes exerted their effect on one. Under effective psychotherapy, some of them may change very greatly, quite swiftly, and particularly fortunate experience unrelated to intentional therapeutic interventions may be equally effective." [11]

The various personifications which we develop from infancy on "grow" and change in a manner somewhat analogous to the history of real people. These personifications are symbolic representations of past experiences. Perhaps some of these things will gradually become clearer as I come to discuss the self-system. According to Sullivan, the complement of eidetic people each one of us "carries with us and lives with" originate from the rudimentary personifications of infancy, which in adult language, are referred to as the Good Mother associated with relaxation of the tensions of needs and the Bad Mother associated with the experiences of anxiety.

Please do not think that anything like an adult recognition of a person is meant in connection with infantile experience of the Good or Evil Mother. They are meant to signify only vaguely differentiated interpersonal experiences of the two kinds I mentioned.[12] In other words, they are inferential constructions whose plausibility or heuristic value could be demonstrated only in several papers.

Until recently it was customary among students of man to set off the biological from the cultural, and to speak of the two as if they almost existed side by side. Psychology texts, for exam-

---

[11] "Multidisciplined Coordination of Interpersonal Data" in *Culture and Personality*, edited by S. Stansfeld Sargent and Marian W. Smith, Viking Fund, New York, 1949, p. 189.

[12] See the *Conceptions*, pp. 38-39. Sullivan in recent years devoted many lectures to the evolution of signs, symbols and symbolic behavior but it is impossible to discuss these things briefly with any clarity.

ple, would discuss the "social factors" in psychology. But this is misleading and reminds one of the old conception of man as a twofold being. From the beginning of life one is exposed to the influences, to the attitudes and modes of behavior, of others who take care of the infant and without whose care the infant cannot live. These "others" are "carriers" of the culture. As I shall show later the infant reacts dynamically to this state of affairs. So there is no way of separating the strictly "biological" from the cultural. As Sullivan expressed this, man-the-animal is known only as new-born. You cannot infer from the behavior of adults what a non-personalized adult of, say, forty-five would be like. The inborn potentialities of man-the-animal which take many years to develop are remarkably labile, subject to durable change by inter-personal experience.

The new-born shows what Sullivan called integrating tendencies, but these he said are not very far from what a biologist might mean by adjustive potentialities. Human instincts Sullivan regarded as "a peculiarly offensive extravagance of language." So he sometimes spoke in terms of adaptive potentialities. In familiar language an adaptive potentiality refers to the ability of the organism to respond to inner or outer stimuli. Only the notion of inner and outer stimuli suggests a rigid dichotomy of "inner and outer" which was foreign to Sullivan's thought. Motivational systems are closely connected with adaptive potentialities in a way which I hope to illustrate presently.

Adaptive potentialities are sufficiently segregated in connection with man's somatic organization that one may speak about zones of interaction, such as the mouth, the oral zone. This zone is said to be a remarkable organization of receptor organs which, so to speak, can "notice" events impinging on it, of "eductor equipment" by which, or with the aid of which, sentience is elaborated, translated into personal meaning, and effector organs by which action and change ensue. From very early in life these three psychobiological substrates make possible the representation in awareness of tensions, activities for satisfactions, and actions for the minimizing of anxiety. While experience and behavior are total rather than local or partial, the conception of zones singles out significant phases of the organism-environment relationships.

Psychiatry in the sense in which I am trying to explain now abandoned the traditional separation of observational data into the subjective and objective. Sullivan does not accept mind as its basic conception as traditional psychology used to do. Nor does he accept the individual human organism, as does psychobiology.[13] He did not consider the person, he says, as an individual who can be abstracted from a social context for the purpose of study, or analysis, but instead as a purely hypothetical entity which is susceptible of study only in interpersonal relations. The unit of study is an interpersonal situation always involving more than one "individual," and for such reasons psychiatry studies by participant observation. The psychiatrist is part of the situation he studies. In other words, he studies the psychological "performances" which occur with him, and of which he is a part, as well as with others.

Interpersonal situations are of course not static. They are constituted by dynamic interpersonal processes. In such a situation some tendency system is integrated, some impulse or dynamic component is expressed, resolved or frustrated, some satisfaction is achieved or some need is aggravated, and the situation is normally ended. When a situation is ended, it becomes a memory, an experience stored up, as it were, which may provide insight for future use in other situations. Also a tendency system may be "multiply-determined," that is, a known impulse, a witting impulse, and an unknown, an unwitting, impulse may find expression in the situation. When a need is frequently frustrated or aggravated, I might add, that kind of experience also under some circumstances provides expectations, of which one may or may not be aware, of future unhappy, frustrating, painful or injurious experiences in similar situations.

Now how are we to define integrating tendencies? In terms of their goals, their end-states, primarily, which may be conscious (represented in awareness or capable of easy recollection) or

13 Psychiatry is also "sui generis." According to Sullivan it is no more a branch of medicine than it is a branch of a social science.

not.[14] Integrating tendencies can be active, can operate, situations can exist, without the people concerned experiencing emotion or at least being conscious of it.

Integrating tendencies in early infancy are to be construed largely as potentialities (if one makes due allowance for what has matured or partly matured so far) in a manner which I will indicate in a moment. They cannot be confused as far as infants are concerned with motives as motives are usually understood. In other words, drives, impulses or whatever become socially defined, developed in the process of acculturation.

Sullivan differentiated human behavior, including reverie processes, dreams, thought, into two interrelated classes, two grand divisions of goals. In other words, he distinguished two broad categories of interpersonal tendencies. The first he called the pursuit of satisfactions. These have a conspicuous relationship to the somatic organization of man and to his biological heritage. The second, the pursuit of security, has to do more obviously with the development of human potentialities in a sociocultural setting. Of the first group, the pursuit of satisfactions, a prime example is hunger. The latter is more clearly derivative of culture, of the assimilation of what is man-made which has gone into one's education and acculturation, by which one becomes a human being. It is related to what Sullivan means by the pursuit of security, which does *not* mean the pursuit of $100,000 a year. Security here has a special meaning which I hope gradually to clarify. It refers roughly to what we mean by the maintenance of self-esteem. The absence of this state of security or, more precisely, its opposite is called anxiety. The collision of the needs for satisfactions, with the need for security, for self-respect and self-esteem often leads to what Sullivan called "conflictful integrations" which are so outstanding in psychiatric work. In essence, security means a feeling that one enjoys the respect of

[14] A comprehensive discussion of goal-seeking would have to take account of the role of intelligence or "reason," the role of socially defined goals, the availability of means toward goals, etc. See Robert K. Merton, *Social Theory and Social Structure,* The Free Press of Glencoe, Illinois, 1949, on the latter.

the other person in a situation and that one respects oneself.

It is the opposition, the conflict of integrating tendencies directed toward the securing of satisfactions with those directed toward the achievement of security, for the feeling of personal worth, of self-esteem and the esteem of others, which provide the fundamental "description" of mental disorder.[15] The healthy development of personality is said to be in large measure the result of an unusually unwitting but still prescribed acculturation or socialization *timed* to meet the biological possibilities of the underlying animal. Some of the profound problems of personality and research, Sullivan used to say in his lectures, originate from the premature application of cultural prescriptions, etc., which have at the time no yet evident biological basis. For example, he believed that a mother's premature efforts at toilet training can have serious consequences for the child, and will, or may, lead to "queer results" which will interpenetrate a great deal of the latter's behavior from then on.

Because the three modes of experience I am about to discuss briefly are concerned with the adaptive capacities of the human being, I want to call attention to the *adaptive* function of signs.[16]

Experience is a term that I shall have to use often. As Sullivan defined it, experience is "anything lived, undergone or the like." Our contact with and in the world is mediated by our capacity to experience. This capacity to experience, he observed, is in turn conditioned by biological potentiality, its state of maturity, the results obtained by previous experience and by the foresight of the neighboring future. All these things condition the capacity to undergo change and set limits to the possibilities of experience. Anxiety, for example, as I shall develop later, sets grave limits to our capacity to undergo educative experience and possible change.

[15] The feeling of self-esteem refers to one's power or ability "to approve oneself as personified or to disapprove oneself, and to encourage or forbid the manifestation of impulses by the other one with whom one is in an interpersonal situation." Quoted from an unpublished lecture by permission of the William Alanson White Psychiatric Foundation. See copyright page.

[16] Compare C. I. Lewis, *An Analysis of Knowledge and Valuation*, Open Court Pub. Co., La Salle, Ill., 1946.

One of the most important things to notice in this theory I am trying to set before you is that experience is essentially symbolic. A very obvious example is the kind of experience this audience now has listening to me. I might add here that Sullivan's use of the term "symbol" is very broad and often includes experiences which others do not class as symbolic.

Sullivan suggested that experience occurs in three significantly different modes, formal distinctions of at least three kinds differentiated in experience which I shall summarize briefly now: the prototaxic, parataxic and syntaxic. The first, the prototaxic, is said to include all the experience of the very early months of life before the infant is presumed to have a self in the distinctive sense adults speak of, before the "I" in the usual sense becomes a center of reference, before experience is differentiated in terms of time and space, of here and there, of before, now, after, etc. (To differentiate is to sort out a significant pattern or patterns from everything else in one's experience.) The fact that the prototaxic mode is pre-verbal does not define its essential characteristic. According to Sullivan, the primordial element of knowing is to differentiate certain elements of prototaxic experience which are connected with, that is, chiefly by being distinguished as different from, one's experience when the characterizing thing is not there.

The prototaxic is followed by the parataxic when rudimentary differentiations of experience are occurring, which is said to make up a good deal of our experience. Its essential characteristic is concomitance or coincidence of experiences, not logical connection. The elements of experience are not related in a logical way. Dreams often, though not always, are a good example of this kind of experience, of this form of symbol operation. But much of our waking experiences also occurs in this mode. And it is well suited to our prejudices.[17]

The third mode, the syntaxic, is characterized by what Sullivan called "consensual validation." That is, to the degree that observation, analysis and what Sullivan, following Charles Spearman, called the eduction of relations is subjected to consensual

[17] For a discussion of parataxic distortions see the *Conceptions of Modern Psychiatry*, pp. 45-46, 100-101.

validation with others, it eventuates in experience in the syntaxic mode. Consensual validation does not mean absolute correctness. It means such agreement with a significant other which "permits fairly exact communication by speech or otherwise, and the drawing of generally useful inferences about the action and thought of the other." [18] Sullivan notes that syntaxic experience is bound by the prescriptions and limitations of the culture. Probably the only exceptions are those of rigorous logical and scientific thinking and testing.

By and large, any thing, any experience that a person can discuss, is experience in the parataxic or syntaxic mode. Anything that can be discussed, he says, is always interpenetrated by elements of the near past or distant past, and prospective future. The anticipations and expectations which one has play a powerful role in activity, in the way one acts.

I have to add a qualification here. According to Sullivan, even experience which never had a representational component is sometimes not beyond the possibility of some kind of recall. When you talk or communicate in such a way that the other fellow has "some idea" of what you are talking about, you are in the syntaxic mode. We often think that what we say and try to communicate are in the syntaxic mode when actually they are parataxic. Sullivan believed that our experiences throughout life occur in the three modes, that, for example, much of our experience is in the prototaxic mode.

Summing up the discussion of the three modes, I have tried to indicate that some actions, behavior, occur in the the prototaxic mode and are unwitting, "unconscious." This is characteristic of early infancy, where differentiations in experience are either lacking or rudimentary and are mainly characterized by succession only. Yet the infant can gradually discover favorable change connected with certain actions. But adults also undergo experience in the prototaxic mode, unwittingly, "unconsciously" with no or almost no felt or representational aspect in focal awareness and therefore with little discrimination of what is happening. From the era of childhood, or before, and onward, we undergo some experience syntaxically, experience which is sufficiently dis-

[18] "Multidisciplined Coordination of Interpersonal Data," p. 177.

criminated and differentiated so that we can give the other fellow *some idea* of what we have in mind or feel. There is in the third instance an intervening mode of experience which begins in infancy, the parataxic mode. Many of our experiences even as adults occur in this mode. In other words, so much of culture is non-rational, not to say irrational, that we do not have the time even if we have the capacity to analyze it so that a good part of our experiences occur in the parataxic mode. There is the additional fact that for many activities, like dressing in the morning, there is neither necessity nor time for precise discriminations of awareness of our experiences, including our actions.

Some additional complexities concerning the three modes occur which I omit. In fact it would take several hours to show how Sullivan worked them into his theories. Nevertheless, some of these distinctions will probably require more clarification.

There are a few more terms which I must try to define or at least suggest their meaning before taking up the developmental history of a person as Sullivan understood it.[19] The first is empathy, which is not in too good repute. Empathy is not supposed to occur through ordinary sensory channels, or if it does, it is not understood how. There is said to be what Sullivan called "a peculiar emotional relationship" between the infant and the significant adult, usually the mother. If the mother is upset, anxious, or hostile, such a feeling or experience is said to be conveyed *somehow* to the infant, so that his sense of well-being, his euphoria is lessened, is decreased. This interchange creates what we as adults know as anxiety in the infant. And it, namely, empathy, is fundamental to understanding the processes of acculturation, socialization, education as outlined in this lecture. I might add that empathy is not by any means confined to infancy. Dr. Fromm-Reichmann, for example, speaks of an empathic linkage between her and some of her patients.[20]

Another term is dynamism. In the literature you read of psychic mechanisms, another of those curious phrases, which

[19] In this paper I do not concern myself with certain logical problems and refinements regarding "specification," "definition," etc.

[20] *Principles of Intensive Psychotherapy*, University of Chicago Press, 1950.

springs from what is to me Freud's logically unsuccessful efforts to formulate psychological theory in terms of nineteenth-century, perhaps I should say, eighteenth- or seventeenth-century mechanism. In any case, dynamism is defined as "a relatively enduring configuration of energy which manifests itself in characterizable processes in interpersonal relations." Dynamism refers to the way in which energy systems are organized and channeled in the human organism. It is said to imply only a relatively enduring capacity to bring about change.

Energy means only what physicists talk about, not psychic energy. Energy Whitehead once defined as merely the name for the quantitative aspect of a structure of happenings. And so the conception of dynamism takes us back again to primary experience, to happenings, occurrences, processes in human life, to interpersonal relations.[21]

Sullivan was the most empirically minded of any psychoanalytically-oriented major psychiatric theorist I know of. He was hostile to broad generalizations unsupported by little if any evidence, which purport to inform us as to the way things are. He was fond of meeting rash statements with the query, "As demonstrated by what?"

Having, I hope, given some idea of the fundamental conceptions, notions and terms used, I surmise the best way to acquaint you with it in at least some detail is to outline what are called the stages, eras, epochs of personality development. They are:

Infancy, which is said to exist up to the maturation of the capacity for language behavior;

Childhood, to the maturation of the capacity for living with compeers;

The Juvenile Era, to the maturation of the capacity for intimacy with a member of one's own sex, what has been called isophilic intimacy;

Preadolescence, to the maturation of the capacity for intimacy with a member of the other sex;

Early adolescence, to the patterning of lustful behavior;

Late Adolescence, to maturity.

[21] It is philosophically naive to assume that one must postulate a libido, or general life force in order to account for human behavior.

Because the infant is helpless if unaided by others, he needs a great variety of what Sullivan calls tender actions by the mothering one, such as the provision of food and water, the removal of waste products, the protection of body temperature, and, he believed, physical contact with the mothering one.[22] The activity of the infant arising from the tension of needs is said to induce tension in the mothering one, which is experienced as tenderness, which Sullivan characterized as an impulsion to activities toward the relief or satisfaction of the infant's needs. This activity of the mothering one concerning the relief of the infant's needs is presently experienced by the infant as the undergoing of tender behavior. Please notice that tenderness as understood here is no mere subjective or inner or psychic state. And in general this applies to Sullivan's theories. Thus the need for tenderness is ingrained as an interpersonal need from the beginning. According to Sullivan, since tenderness is indispensable to the infant's and young child's survival, it creates a universal tendency to manifest tenderness even though it may later have to be disintegrated.

With one exception, which is perhaps not too firmly established, that is, the need for contact, the first needs that fall under the genus of the need for tenderness are tensions, disequilibria which arise in the necessary communal existence of the infant and the physical-chemical world. It is, however, as he says, not merely a matter of a bigger and better incubator. The mother or mothering one behaves tenderly, deriving pleasure from responding to the manifestations of the infant's needs, and helps to relieve various recurrent disequilibria, various needs.[23] The term disequilibrium is not a mere fancy word for a familiar thing; it emphasizes the fact of the infant's communal existence with and by means of the environment.

[22] For a brief summary of the various stages, see "Tensions Interpersonal and International: A Psychiatrist's View," by Sullivan, in *Tensions That Cause Wars*, edited by Hadley Cantril, University of Illinois Press, Urbana, 1950; and the *Conceptions of Modern Psychiatry*.

[23] She has the principal role of not only keeping the infant alive but of providing the basic patterns of being human. She is the first model. In imitative play, the child acts like the mother for fun. Also he is said to act like mother in order to obtain various satisfactions and avoid her disapproval.

Tension is potentiality for action and it may or may not have a felt or representational aspect. It is a demand for certain energy transformations, such as occur with the ingestion of food. There is no need—it is in fact confusing theoretically—to add an adjective like "mental" or "psychic," in which you get "mental" or "psychic tensions."

So far I have been talking about real tension, tension that we undergo in varying degrees probably twenty-four hours of the day. If we extrapolate extreme instances of this we get what is called absolute tension, which is an "ideal" construct. The nearest approach to this in actuality is said to be the rather uncommon and always relatively transient state of terror. The reciprocal of absolute tension, speaking mathematically, is absolute euphoria, where there is no tension, a state of utter, unalloyed well-being, a state which the angels continually have, if I remember rightly. And the nearest we ever get to that, the greatest degree of real euphoria one ever has, is perhaps when one is an infant in a state of deep sleep.

The sole function of these ideal constructs, of course, is to guide our thoughts about the various degrees of euphoria and of tension people actually undergo.

The tensions which occasionally or recurrently lower the infant's state of well-being, his euphoria, which mark the disequilibration of his being, are those needs which primarily pertain to his communal existence with and by means of the physical-chemical world. The relaxation of those tensions is called by the general term satisfaction.[24]

In the early months of infancy, the alteration of need and satisfaction is, it is inferred, experienced in the prototaxic mode. Gradually the felt discomfort of need, it is said, begins to be differentiated—by which I do not mean what adults mean by conscious differentiation—gradually the discomfort is discriminated in terms of the direction toward its relief, with increasingly clear foresight of relief by appropriate action. In other words, the infant gradually catches on in a dim way to the fact, for example, that the cry which presumably at first arose "spon-

[24] Compare *Logic: The Theory of Inquiry* by John Dewey, Henry Holt & Co., New York, 1938, pp. 26-28.

taneously" brings relief from various discomforts, because of course the mothering one does something about them.

However rudimentary this foresight may be or seem from an adult standpoint it is the beginning of something that is said to be one of the greatly striking things of human in contrast to all other living. Much—if not all—successful living depends on it.

The next thing I want to discuss is anxiety, which, at first, at least, may be induced unwittingly in the infant by the mothering one when she is undergoing what Sullivan calls "noxious emotional states." It is not known, at least Sullivan did not know, how early, but somewhere in the first months of life, anxiety is manifested. It is said to be utilized in some societies a little, and in some a great deal in "training" the human animal to become a person more or less according to the norms and prescriptions of the society.

Anxiety is in Sullivan's theories a central explanatory conception for psychiatry. According to him, many apparently different processes are actually techniques for minimizing or avoiding anxiety. He also explains such things as guilt and shame as complex derivatives of anxiety. A *persona*, made familiar by C. G. Jung, is said to be a characteristic development of people who are made anxious by almost any interpersonal contacts. Such people develop an enormous number of precautionary techniques which serve as a façade behind which they hide in order not to expose themselves to anxiety-provoking attacks. Anxiety is related to and plays a role in the evolution of multiple me-you patterns which in some people operate in lieu of a consistent mode of interpersonal relations where profound uncertainty characterizes one's evaluation of personal worth, and a lack of any clear "valuational system." [25]

While the tensions I discussed before, with possibly one exception, pertain primarily to the physical-chemical environment, the tension of anxiety pertains to the infant's communal existence with a personal environment, a human world. The relaxation of

[25] See "Psychiatry: Introduction to the Study of Interpersonal Relations," *Psychiatry*, 1938, 1: 121-134. Reprinted in *A Study of Interpersonal Relations*, edited by Patrick Mullahy, Hermitage Press, 1949.

this tension is the experience of security, of interpersonal security.

It is said to be distinguished, when early experienced, from all other reductions of euphoria, such as those I mentioned, by the absence of anything specific. There is, therefore, as it is first experienced, little or no differentiation in terms of the direction towards its relief by appropriate action. The infant is said to lack the capacity for such action. This means that the infant cannot develop foresight of its relief as he is said to do in regard to the tensions of somatic needs. No action of the infant is said to be consistently and frequently associated with the relief of anxiety. The events which evoke anxiety in the infant can neither be removed nor destroyed nor escaped. Only a change in the other person will assuage or banish it. Because of limitations of space I shall not discuss the theoretical basis for infantile anxiety. You will find some of the data in Sullivan's *Conceptions of Modern Psychiatry.*

If, for example, the mother is anxious for some reason, because of or by means of the assumed empathic linkage, anxiety is induced in the infant. When she observes the infant is disturbed, she in turn may get more anxious, which means further lowering of the infant's euphoria. Thus, to speak loosely, anxiety is not manageable. Even in adults anxiety is far from being easily manageable. Many, perhaps most, people have little discriminating awareness of anxiety or its causal conditions. It occurs mainly in the parataxic mode.

Anxiety is a tension which opposes needs, as well as actions appropriate to their relief. If one is very anxious, he may not be able to eat, or to keep food down, at least while the anxiety strongly persists. It "interferes with effective alertness to the factors in the current situation that are immediately relevant to its occurrence, and thus with the refinement and precision of action related to its relief or reduction." [26] Whenever anything happens which would seriously disturb or threaten to disturb an established pattern of dealing with others, anxiety intervenes

[26] "The Meaning of Anxiety in Psychiatry and in Life," *Psychiatry,* Vol. 11, No. 1, Feb. 1948, p. 4.

and arouses actions for its abatement. The activities evoked to assuage anxiety are called security operations. Anxiety is the great instrument by which radical, extensive personal change is resisted or prevented. I want to emphasize that anxiety is always related to interpersonal relations. It originates in an interpersonal context and it always operates in such a context.

There is, according to Sullivan, a vast difference between anxiety and fear.[27] Some people say that anxiety is "internal fear," or fear whose cause is unknown, or something on that order. Anxiety in Sullivan's sense cannot be equated with fear, although in infancy anxiety and fear may *feel* the same. Any danger to the existence or biological integrity of the organism arouses fear, whether in a mild form or in the extreme form of terror. Those dangers are said to be in general oxygen starvation, sub-cooling, molar injury or failure of sundry vital processes. This distinction is of the greatest theoretical importance even for infancy. Thus crying may evoke mothering activity which will relieve the fear-provoking circumstances, and crying can become differentiated as action appropriate to bring about relief of fear. When the infant is anxious, due to the presumed empathic linkage crying may result in increased anxiety. In other words, if the anxious mother is made more anxious by her offspring's crying, it may contribute to, may induce, increasing anxiety in the infant. Of course fear and anxiety may occur at times together. One fears a punch in the nose, atomic bombs, the loss of a job in depression.[28] One gets anxious when a person anticipates, whether rightly or not, that the regard of another person will decrease, that his regard and respect for you will become less, or that one's own regard for oneself will decrease. Anxiety is related to the loss of esteem for one by oneself or by others.

When one gets very anxious, one is more or less stymied. First one may not be aware of what is happening to him. It

[27] He defines fear as the foreseen relief of hurt or pain and escape or avoidance of its specific tensions.

[28] This illustration is not taken from Sullivan.

may even take years of analysis before one can become clearly aware of those times when one is anxious, and what the circumstances connected with it are. Of course, ordinarily people do not become that anxious because they have learned more or less willy-nilly how to avoid most severe anxiety-provoking situations and because they have unwittingly learned techniques of disguising anxiety or of neutralizing it by, for example, getting resentful, angry or hostile.[29]

As I have already said, anxiety "interferes with effective alertness to the factors in the current situation that are immediately relevant to its occurrence, and thus with the refinement and precision of action related to its relief or reduction." Ordinarily fear does not have such a paralyzing effect on awareness, and it "is commonly manifested in activity which removes (destroys) the provocative situational factors, escapes them, neutralizes their importance, or defers being afraid to the near future."[30]

When a person has been considerably exposed to and influenced by anxiety from significant others, useful learning and understanding of many phases of living will be greatly reduced. Profiting by experience will be greatly handicapped. Anything— an overt act, the use of a word or a thought, a feeling—which is heavily invested with anxiety becomes automatically inhibited, distorted, or somehow made complex by the intervention of the self. In a situation when the other person provokes anxiety in oneself, one's "personification" of that other individual changes rapidly, and, very likely in a negative direction. If this were not so, if this more or less automatic function of anxiety did not occur, there would be, as Sullivan observes, much less mental illness in the world, at least in the Western world. There would be less pain, less irrational feeling, less prejudice, less hostility, less despair; and instead of forever more or less blindly repeating unwise acts, some people to a large extent, and probably all people to some extent, would learn ways of life which would entail

[29] A very good way of avoiding anxiety, Sullivan claims, is to foresee disapproval of others. Thus one would often be in a better position to counteract it.

[30] "The Meaning of Anxiety," p. 4.

much less misery and far more joy to mankind.[31] There is, I think, good reason to believe that anxiety operates to some degree among people in every society. There is every reason to believe that it operates to an enormous degree in our society.

The self-system (self-dynamism) is built up to an enormous extent so that one will not again encounter a particular anxiety-provoking situation. I will discuss the self presently. Here I might add in passing that a great deal of what Sullivan called poor work in psychiatry was, he thought, either directly or indirectly related to self-system functions both in psychiatrist and patient.

I want to mention briefly the notion of covert processes, processes that are subject to inference only, rather than direct observation. According to Sullivan, toward the end of infancy there occurs what he named delay in behavior. This occurs because needs manifest a hierarchical organization. Hunger, for example, takes precedence over something else going on. The hunger interrupts the latter. Later, after hunger has been satisfied, the interrupted activity is resumed, though with some change. The inference is that something went on in connection with the interrupted activity. Sullivan believed that "amazingly early" in postnatal life, covert symbol operations, prototaxic and parataxic, in connection with needs occur in a rudimentary form.

As time passes in infancy, euphoria becomes increasingly associated with the experience of activity, of doing things, of activities from wiggling one's fingers to God knows what. The euphoria associated with activity is called the pleasure, the feeling of well-being associated with the manifestation of ability or power. Sullivan says the first "theorem" of interpersonal relations is: The exercise of an ability is inherently pleasure-giving, or pleasant. Abilities, of course, are exercised through, by means of, dynamisms. The ability to speak, for example, is exercised through the oral dynamism. A corollary to this exercise of an ability theorem is: The maturation of any capacity, the realization of any ability, creates a need to exercise this ability. There have to be maturation of the capacity and appropriate and useful experience. Perhaps, needless to say, genetically determined

[31] This statement should not be construed as advocating a social panacea for the political and economic problems of the world.

dynamisms underlie and fix the envelope of possible development of dynamisms. In simple language, the "genetically given"
fixes the limits of possibility.

I want to add a caution here. The conception of dynamism
includes much more than those things that are "fixed" or relatively "fixed" by "elaborate apparatus" in the nerves, muscles,
glands, etc. Its essential meaning is at least recurrently demonstrated potentiality for bringing about a characterizable change.
It cannot be equated with, or located in, specific physiological
apparatus.

The first of all learning, that is, what Sullivan calls the initial
discrimination in the previously all-encompassing vague and un-
differentiated world of the infant, is presumed to be evoked in
order to avoid recurrence of severe anxiety. The infant, it is inferred, gradually learns to discriminate increasing from diminishing anxiety and to alter his activity in the direction of the latter.
And before he is many months old, he is said to show sublimation, that is, he will have unwittingly adopted some pattern of
activity which will partially satisfy a need and avoid the anxiety
provoked by an activity which would otherwise in the absence
of anxiety bring optimum satisfaction. The residue of the need
will be discharged for example in processes later described as
reverie processes and especially, it is said, by this sort of activity
in sleep. Sublimation does not at any time include any conscious
lucid thinking about it. It occurs in the parataxic mode, where
connections and relations of experiences, other than sheer coincidence or concomitance are not noted.

I shall not take time to discuss Sullivan's ideas about things
like trial and success learning, and pantomime which probably
everyone is familiar with in a general way.[32]

[32] Sullivan mentions various types of learning which occur, starting with
infancy: learning by or from the anxiety gradient, that is learning to differentiate increasing from decreasing anxiety, trial and error learning, both
from human example and otherwise, learning from the experience of rewards and punishments, learning from the eduction of relations. Sullivan
also says that the first great educative experience is anxiety, unqualified, by
which I assume he means that it begins to provoke some sort of rudimentary
alertness, even before the infant starts to learn from the anxiety gradient.

Now I want to talk briefly about the beginnings of the self-system. It is said that from the experience of rewards, that is, of approval, parental tenderness, learning by the anxiety gradient, etc., there occurs in childhood an initial "personification" of three phases of experience, which will presently be "me," the "me" being invariably connected with some sentience of the body. The initial "personifications" are "not-me," "good-me," and "bad-me."[33]

"Good me" is explained as "the growing organization of experience in which satisfactions have been enhanced by rewarding increments in tenderness from the mothering one." "Bad me" is "organized experience in the association of increasing degrees of anxiety with behavior involving the mothering one . . ." "Not me" refers to some of the most poorly grasped aspects of living by a person and is not constituted by communicative processes. It is an "unusually simple, parataxic sort of personification of poorly grasped aspects of living which will presently be regarded as dreadful and still later will be differentiated into incidents which are attended by awe or by horror or loathing, far the greater number of encounters with which personification occur in the phase of living to which we refer as dreaming-while-asleep." [34] Acquaintance with it is said to be at best marginal, unelaborated observations of others, even though the "others" may sometimes be, or be similar to, mythological figures.

By and large "good me" and "bad me" only belong to the self-system or dynamism which is an organization of educative experience developed by the necessity to escape or minimize anxiety. More exactly stated, the two become differentiated as belonging to, as being the "underpinnings" of, the personification

[33] "Not-me" is said to be very striking in its indirect manifestations in dissociated behavior.

Good-me and bad-me represent a parataxic ordering of experienced events. A great deal of what we learn as children is said to be incomprehensible and is learned by rote. The personification "me" is the outcome of a development in the syntaxic mode of experience. This syntaxic "novelty" is said to be a wonderful discovery and can "always" be depended on—in contrast to good- and bad-me.

[34] Quoted from an unpublished lecture by permission of the William Alanson White Psychiatric Foundation. See copyright page.

meaning

"me," which is a part of the self-dynamism. The self begins to be elaborated in or from the necessity to discriminate forbidding gestures which mean or portend increasing anxiety.[35] So the self is born of anxiety-provoking situations in infancy, childhood and in fact throughout life. In a loose manner of speaking, the self more or less controls awareness. While the self is *not* entirely synonymous with consciousness, thinking in the usual sense of the word is governed by the self largely in a manner congenial to it. Thinking, of course, occurs by means of symbols. This means that the use of symbols is largely governed by the requirements of the self. And for that reason, the meaning of a symbol, or part of the meaning (or meanings) may escape the one who uses it.

It is not possible to discuss Sullivan's more recent formulations of the self adequately short of a series of papers. Now I can mention only a few ideas which I hope may communicate a partial understanding of it to you. The "roots" of the self are said to be fixed in the last third of infancy. According to Sullivan, the infant gradually differentiates situations where it is better to endure certain discomforts rather than that which would follow action for their relief. Action for their relief might, for example, bring disapproval (forbidding gestures[36]) of the mothering one, and hence anxiety in the infant. It is at this point, it is said, when the infant begins the long, long "task" of being a human being by remaining somewhat tense so that he will have some chance of getting some relaxation and sleep instead of having to endure states of intense anxiety.

On this basis Sullivan formulated a so-called theorem: "Anxiety, or the foresight or anticipation of anxiety, makes desirable the maintenance of certain tensions, discomforts, insofar as they ward off, prevent the occurrence of, or alleviate anxiety."[37] The avoidance of anxiety becomes an end in itself, that is, the main-

---

[35] In childhood one learns that the parents are not "uniformly omniscient" in distinguishing one's goodness from one's badness, so that one becomes uncertain, to a degree, concerning the approval and disapproval one's actions will evoke. One may become uncertain as to who one is or is taken to be, that is, one's personal integrity is to that extent undermined.

[36] These include frowns and changes in an accustomed voice of the mothering one.

tenance of *relative euphoria* by continued discomfort is called the maintenance of interpersonal security, said to be ultimately most significant as the experience of self-esteem.

The self-dynamism is "the relatively enduring organization of processes which manifests itself in situations related to former experiences of anxiety; which situations it tends to change, and this change is in the particular way that avoids the occurrence of, or minimizes the severity of, anxiety." [37] Hence the self is a product of interpersonal relations. It is experienced in terms of suiting the requirements of other people, who include imaginary others, so that one may avoid or minimize anxiety and maintain the gradually evolved experience of "self-satisfaction" or self-esteem. It is an "elaboration of experience" chiefly by association with reductions in euphoria, and is definable only by reference to, or in terms of, the person and others.

I do not have the space to attempt to explain in detail how, according to Sullivan, there comes about a restriction of freedom of activities designed to satisfy needs, or how foresight of satisfaction of need is altered, or how satisfaction itself becomes modified. The point is that activities and experiences are altered and channeled, structured in certain ways due chiefly to the induction of anxiety in the growing, developing youngster by the mothering one.[38] In this way the self-dynamism evolves and becomes elaborated in late infancy, childhood and thereafter. It operates in situations related to or "reminiscent of" former experiences of anxiety. In other words, whenever a person finds himself in a situation where, due to past experience, he anticipates the possibility or likelihood of anxiety, he does something which is calculated to avoid the occurrence of anxiety.

All of this involves a certain channeling and restriction of what a person notices, what he is conscious of, and what he selectively ignores or inattends, and what he has to dissociate. May I

[37] Quoted from an unpublished lecture by permission of William Alanson White Psychiatric Foundation. See copyright page.

[38] For example, needs which are said to be originally differentiated from all other disturbances of euphoria by increasingly clear foresight of their relief by appropriate activity become modified in the direction of a specific blend or experience of felt need and circumscribing threat of anxiety.

remind you that all this occurs in relation to others, at first the mothering one, later, brothers, sisters, playmates, teachers, friends, colleagues? The self is an organization of interpersonal processes, experiences, relations, structured according to, or in relation to, former experiences of anxiety.

"As a result of the modifications of, you might say, the whole impulsive base of living," Sullivan claims, "or at least a very large part of it, that which is covered by or touched by, social definitions and prescriptions and rights and requirements, duties and responsibilities, there comes into being in childhood the pleasure in tension . . . Now that does not mean that all tensions are pleasant—very far from it. But it means that tensions which have come into being through the action of the self-dynamism in connection with other impulses of the person, that these tensions come to be enjoyable—you might say loosely, because they are reassuring——." [39]

The pleasure in tension is said to fall under two genera: specific rigidities in posture and specific alertness or vigilance which is chiefly exercised to restrict the freedom of awareness. Due to various experiences of anxiety, of approval, of disapproval, of trial and error learning from human example, of the eduction of relations, that is, in ordinary language, making inferences, putting things together, discovering relationships, etc., the youngster gradually develops certain attitudes about himself and others. Maintaining felt interpersonal security, self-esteem, becomes manifested as the ability to approve and reprove impulses and action of the personified self, that to which we refer when we say "myself," and to encourage and forbid the expression of impulses by others.

I might add here that the experience of *powerlessness* to reprove, encourage, disapprove by the self, or in Sullivan's language, "in the field of the self-dynamism," is hate, that is, the anticipation of extremely severe anxiety.

The self-dynamism is built up from experience, and this experience has more or less of a pattern. And so the self, which is born of interpersonal experience, has describable characteristics.

[39] Quoted from an unpublished lecture by permission of the William Alanson White Psychiatric Foundation. See copyright page.

It is inherent in the nature of the self to tend strongly to maintain the characteristics which it acquires in early life in order to
avoid anxiety, or at least to keep it at a minimum.[40] Further, the
self is the "reflection in personality" of the culture, which contains various incoherencies not conducive to a rational development of the self. And so the self-dynamism tends strongly to
escape the influence of experience that is incongruous with its
current organization and functional activity.

For such reasons one can see why the self is "no friend" of
the therapist in his work with the patient because of the threat
of change. Hence the therapist has to know how or to learn how
to circumvent the "resistance" of the self to change.

As one progresses into childhood, the parents carry on deliberate training in the folkways in the hope that their offspring will
grow to be the sort of person considered desirable, admirable if
possible, in their society or community or class. They must do
this if their offspring is going to have a chance to be a "success"
in life, that is, in terms of contentment or happiness, as well as
being "a credit" to them, or at least not a "disgrace." Otherwise
he will be or may be subject to the misery, defeat and despair
which often befalls those considered not "right" by society, not
"adequate," or even "crazy." However, as Sullivan observes, the
home can scarcely reflect all the significant features of the "culture complex" of the community.[41]

Throughout childhood, when speech is learned, there occurs
a rapid and sometimes enormous growth "in the expressible content" of the self, related and fixed to the symbol "I." As I have

[40] This statement does not imply that the person necessarily will be
successful at warding off severe anxiety. It depends largely on the structure
of the self whether one will be or not.

[41] Hence the enormous importance in our society of the school, the
church, and other agencies of "education" and communication like the
newspaper, the radio, television, the moving picture for the "socializing
process." Sullivan notes that a person brought up in a home in which there
were great deviations from the cultural norms, where there was great freedom from conventional prejudices, for example, would be provided with
very poor preparation for what he would have to encounter when he reaches
the point where he becomes immersed in the culture complex reflected in
the school.

indicated, the two personifications of "good me" and "bad me"
become identified as belonging to the personified self ("I") which
is an aspect of the developing self-system.

Selective inattention is said to be the most frequent manifestation of restriction of awareness by the self. In selective inattention one does not clearly note some relevant factor in a
situation. One does not develop any clear awareness of its character, of its significance. One's attention has to be *recalled* to the
factor or factors in question in order to be clear about them.
Selective inattention differs from concentration, where one's attention *is* focussed more or less on the relevant factors, and from
"preoccupation," that is the occupation of awareness by a kind of
psychological "busy work."

In therapeutic work, the participant-observer, the therapist,
discovers that the patient consistently fails to notice and to understand certain aspects of situations, of interpersonal situations in
which he is integrated, whether with the therapist or otherwise.
And, further, any tentative calling attention to these unnoted aspects is likely to arouse the anxiety or anger of the patient. In
fact, clumsy handling of such unnoted behavior may arouse unbearable anxiety on the part of the patient, and he may not return. These interpersonal processes which ordinarily cannot be
noted, cannot be understood, and cannot be assimilated into the
self are, by definition, dissociated. They occur outside conscious
awareness, conscious being defined as the easily recollectable
series of experienced events. Stated differently, the self does not
recognize those processes, and in general disavows them. Because
of the structure, the organization of the self, they cannot be recognized because they would arouse unbearable anxiety, and in
certain cases terror.

According to Sullivan, whenever matured abilities have to be
suppressed because of intense anxiety or in addition certain types
of interferences with the youngster's comfort and freedom occur, and when all of this happens before he can have any idea
of what is happening, there are said to be gradually differentiated within personality a group of shadowy, never clearly conscious, inconceivable and unpersonified experiences, which in
adult language one might say are marked "not of me." There

are *no* referential formulations and elaborations of such experiences.

The development of tendency systems consisting of the not-me has occurred in connection with appalling experiences whose feeling tones are suggested by the words: horror, loathing, awe and dread. These events, the events so marked, have not been subjected to cognitive processes within conscious awareness. They originate from intense experiences of anxiety in infancy and subsequently.

I have suggested to you that, according to Sullivan, the infant's and child's behavior, such as manipulating the region around the anus, can be inhibited because of the empathic linkage *before* there is any formulation that could be called having an idea of the thing that is inhibited. And it is from this sort of experience there develops, according to Sullivan, the not-me phase of personality. Sullivan's conception of the not-me grows out of mostly retrospective analysis of certain experiences and it in general is only inferentially knowable.

Although, it is said, some such components probably exist in everyone, they become significant or greatly significant under the following circumstances: when the child in the juvenile era is practically incapable of controlling ways of behavior, ways of thinking, which expose him to severe humiliations, to intense anxiety, in the society of his compeers or authoritarian non-parental adults.[42] What may have been a previously relatively harmless component of personality of the "not me," may have added to it a "rather important component of childhood personality," which since it leads to unbearable anxiety in juvenile society is assimilated to it—the whole existing in dissociation;[43] and then the painful processes no longer harass one, and fade from the attention of others.

If the original tendency did not exist as not-me, the com-

[42] Compare the *Conceptions of Modern Psychiatry*, p. 22.

[43] The details of Sullivan's explanation are too complicated for brief summary. The main point is that if a person is to manifest or indicate a dissociation of important motivational systems the grounds for it shall probably have been prepared very early in life. Dissociation is not, of course, confined to experiences in the early part of life.

ponent of childhood personality, it is said, would have nothing
exterior to the self to "attach" itself to. If the original component
did not exist, two other possibilities would remain for the now
painful system of tendencies. The now-forbidden—that is anx-
iety-provoking-in-the-presence-of-compeers—motivational system
could either be disintegrated, or overtly continued while the
child suffers the consequences—he is avoided, disliked, or hated.
The general principle is said to be "that which collides fatally
with the environment, at stage after stage, if *possible* is disintegrated and comes out partly as something you do in your
sleep and in stages of absent-mindedness, and partly what you
do [overtly] and earn social approval." [44] Nevertheless, if once
acceptable tendency systems cannot be disintegrated they will,
if possible, be dissociated. And when they are dissociated, they
will be elaborated, developed in the course of life events. One
who has them will not note them. The dissociated tendency will
not be observed because experience pertaining to it will evoke
selective inattention or obsessive substitutive acts and preoccupations. They may however be indicated to a psychiatric observer
by such things as automatisms, by reports of terrifying experiences in sleep, and in other ways.

Traditionally, some people have thought that matters pertaining to sex were what were dissociated. In Sullivan's view this is a
much too simple idea.

When a disastrous failure of dissociation occurs, there is said
to be an "eruption" into awareness of cravings, or abhorrent impulses, there is the occurrence of a fugue, or panic, or both, with
a schizophrenic episode following.[45]

It must be realized that all the tendency systems that survive
in one "grow," that "everything human grows," some fast, some
slowly, whether "in" the self-system or exterior to it. So I want to
emphasize the element of time.

Sullivan distinguished between conjunctive and disjunctive
attitudes in interpersonal relations. The former, in a loose manner of speaking, hold the interpersonal relations together, bring

[44] Quoted from an unpublished lecture by permission of the William
Alanson White Psychiatric Foundation. See copyright page.

[45] Compare the *Conceptions,* lecture IV.

people together toward intimacy, collaboration, or cooperation. The latter tend to break up situations, separate people, put them at cross purposes, prevent something occurring. Ordinarily one might think of love and hate as the examples *par excellence* of conjunctive and disjunctive attitudes.[46] But love is said to be among the very last of human abilities to mature in the course of personality development, and further it is in any case said to be a rather uncommon thing in our society. But attitudes of collaboration and cooperation are not rare. And so, for all these reasons, Sullivan suggests the contrast of tenderness and malevolence instead of love and hate. The undergoing of tenderness, that is, the experience of beneficent activities of the mothering one, in turn promotes in the development in the infant and child an active interest in being tender as is manifested in playing with dolls, etc. But subsequent very unfortunate experience may compel the youngster to dissociate his tender impulses or to disintegrate them.[47]

This brings me to the so-called theorem of reciprocal emotion. Integration in an interpersonal situation is said to be a reciprocal process in which (1) complementary needs are either resolved, or aggravated; (2) complementary patterns of activity are evolved, or they are disintegrated, and (3) foresight of satisfaction, or foresight of *rebuff*, of similar needs is facilitated.

I shall take space to develop only one point now. The complementary patterns of activity in the infant-mother relationship which are developed are *not* for example the activity of the infant in taking nourishment and of the mother in providing the breast, etc., but just the opposite. It is the mothering action, the tender impulses, which the infant gradually develops. Witness the case of children playing with dolls. (Since the mother long since learned to suck a nipple she does not need to evolve that

[46] According to Sullivan, one cannot hate oneself wholesale. One can only hate certain tendencies in oneself.

[47] Another, and less drastic possibility, when the expression of tenderness becomes associated with anxiety, is that it may be "hedged about" with what Sullivan calls precautions. Some people are very guarded as to occasions when they manifest tenderness.

pattern.) So there gradually grows in one a notion of how various needs *in* or of *another* can be satisfied, or if one has had very unfortunate experience, how those needs of another can be rebuffed. This is the way we learn much of what is "fixed" in the culture. We develop complementary needs, complementary patterns of activity to satisfy them, and foresight of complementary satisfactions.

Before going on with examples where such fortunate outcome does not occur, I want to mention the disintegration of tendency-systems and behavior patterns. When a tendency-system is dis-integrated, broken up as though it never existed, there must be either a refinement of the old integration, or a reintegration of the elements of the motivational system disintegrated into new patterns of behavior, or a reactivation of an earlier pattern (regression).

If one suffers recurrent experience of a rebuff of the need for tenderness, a phenomenon said to occur ordinarily in later child-hood and after, there may occur a disintegration of patterns of tender action previously learned, and in turn a development of mischievous and malicious action. The latter, the mischievous and malicious action, occurs in situations characterized by foreseen rebuff. In other words, the unwanted, unloved child whose needs for tenderness are actively thwarted again and again gradually disintegrates his need for tenderness, and replaces, "converts" the disintegrated elements into the opposite of the need for tender-ness so that one will no longer be hurt unbearably. Now as a result one evolves patterns of behavior which in a child are called mischievous or later malevolent or malicious. They hurt, they injure, they cause anxiety in the other fellow. The redefinition of a tendency system such as I have discussed occurs in the para-taxic mode.

The child who is disliked in the home group expects similar treatment from others. And he will therefore, under ordinary circumstances, manifest a hostile attitude toward others, toward anyone becoming significant to him. And he will, of course, not be able to be comfortable let alone happy in his relations with others. As a result of all this, he may engage in belittling, disparaging observations of others, trying to minimize anxiety by "tearing them down."

What about the famed Oedipus complex? [48] In a paper called "Erogenous Maturation" published in the *Psychoanalytic Review*, January, 1926, Sullivan observed that it "must be recognized as a distortion, not as a biological development normal to the male child." It is, he said, "the result of multiple vicious features of our domestic culture." And he went on to elaborate on this point. He also made similar remarks about the Electra complex, saying "I believe we have thrust upon woman altogether too many conclusions derived from the genetic study of the male." While he obviously believes the parent-child relationship is of enormous significance especially during the first two eras, he does not think sex has anything to with this.

The juvenile era is said to be ushered in by the maturation of a need for compeers, for the company of others significantly like one. If no real playmates are available, the child creates imaginary playmates. In this era there is a development of self-reliance in contrast to a hitherto relation of subordination to the significant adults. There is an increasing experience of oneself as reflected now by one's compeers which augments the function of the self-dynamism, Sullivan says, to approve and disapprove manifestations of the personified self. In the juvenile era, there is a growth of social accommodation which includes a great many techniques for getting along with one's compeers, or, in unfortunate instances, isolation. Second, there is a growth of experience in social subordination or rebelliousness. Social subordination means that one can subordinate oneself to others in a social organization without misery. One does not have to be forever at war with the teacher or even in later life with the boss.[49] Third, in the juvenile era the parents lose a good deal of their peculiar attributes and are, so to speak, reduced to life-size as people. The parents are gradually differentiated as special in-

[48] Compare *Oedipus, Myth and Complex* by Patrick Mullahy, Hermitage Press, 1948, p. 315.

[49] This should not be construed as implying anything in particular about industrial and labor relations.

stances of people. Yet people who, save for their inability to identify their parents as people, have had fortunate experience in this era, are said to maintain security in their relations with others even though they never attain maturity and in many ways act more like school children in a great deal of their living. People who were "arrested" in the juvenile era may lead an active sex life, that is, as Sullivan says, their genitals may be busily occupied, but such interpersonal relations as are connected with the genital performances are more like those of the early school years and school society.

In our society, children of the juvenile era go to school, experience of course fraught with considerable consequences for good or evil. In fortunate circumstances, some of the limitations and idiosyncracies of the home are corrected by school experience. The teacher, for instance, by example and precept can correct some of the inadequate experience acquired in the home. Except in the most stable, unchanging phases of social organization, the home is said to constitute an inadequate preparation for life. In this era also the juvenile learns complex skills or improves on things he learned earlier. He learns them from a series of models, which in general means how to be one's age.

Preadolescence is said to be ushered in by the maturation of the need for interpersonal intimacy with a member of one's own sex, namely, a chum. Up to this point, there is normally developed skill in competition and compromise. Now, if all has gone well so far, or at least not too badly, the capacity to love matures.[50] Love exists when and only when the satisfactions and security of the loved one are approximately as important as are one's own.

One finds a "fortunate someone" of one's own sex with whom an unprecedented degree of intimacy can occur. And it is said that the characteristics of one's integration with members of one's own sex in this era set the patterns of integration with one's own sex throughout subsequent eras of personality development.

Because one can communicate on equal terms, on a basis of

[50] Some of the "warps" which characterize the arrival at preadolescence are: a development of precautions against expressing tenderness, a development of malevolent attitudes, a development of social distance without serious anxiety, failure to be one's age or sex, etc.

freedom from anxiety, with another member of the human race, with one's chum, there is a vast exchange of ideas, information, and of the things that one has learned from the folklore of the culture. A comparing of notes, of checking and counter-checking is now possible. There is collaboration.

There develops a new sympathy for the other fellow. Because each one of the two-group ordinarily is likely to have relationships of respect and understanding with other persons (whom the other therefore gets to respect), and because one or more of the latter persons are respected by a number of two-groups, becoming a third member, so to speak, of each, that is, a leader, a linkage of interpersonal relations arises, a real social organization develops, an interlocking social system.[51] Barring psychiatric intervention, preadolescence is said to provide the last chance for markedly favorable change when there has been a previous very unfortunate development of the self.

Certain disastrous eventualities are said to occur in preadolescence. These include: the isolated youth who, for such reasons as invalidism or juvenile unpopularity, finds no chum and must discharge his need for intimacy with a fantastic person; the unduly delayed preadolescent—to whom preadolescence comes, say, two years later than that of the average of those around him —who may, for example, try to relate to younger people than himself and encounter painful social disapproval; the person who moves slowly through preadolescence, who loses his chum because of the latter's maturation and progress to the next stage, an eventuality which may sometimes, for instance, result in "morbid homosexuality," that is, he may get involved in genital-performances with his one-time chum; and there is the person who becomes arrested at preadolescence, who, so to speak, goes no further. In this case, when the genital lust dynamism matures, he directs his lust toward members of his own sex.

I can scarcely do more than mention one or two ideas of Sullivan about loneliness, concerning which he has a great deal to say in his more recent lectures. He says that various compo-

---

[51] Sullivan believed that preadolescence can have "astounding" curative influence. Most of those who arrive at preadolescence with various "warps" may undergo favorable change under the "pressures" of preadolescence.

nents enter into and culminate in the experience of loneliness, which in its full-blown state is fearsome. These components include the need for contact and for tenderness, the need for adult participation in childhood activities, components from the need for compeers,[52] from the need for acceptance, and from the need for intimate exchange with a fellow being. Intimacy is explained as the type of situation consisting of two people which permits validation of all components of personal worth.

Because of its driving force, loneliness can compel a person suffering continued privation of companionship or some more or less satisfactory relationship to brush aside the security operations of the self, even though one may suffer from serious defect of orientation in living.

In other words, it can force even a dreadfully insecure, anxious person, who is isolated because of unfortunate experience in life, to seek companionship. Loneliness is more terrible than anxiety.

As everyone knows, personality gradually evolves and matures. And so: "When, and only when, maturation of capacities has occurred, experience of a valuable kind can occur. *If it does not occur,* if experience is definitely unsuited to providing competence for living with others at this particular level of development, the probabilities of future adequate and appropriate interpersonal relations are definitely and specifically reduced."[53]

It is well to keep that in mind in connection with adolescence. Early adolescence extends from the appearance of the puberty change, or, more accurately, from the movement of interest to members of the other sex to a patterning of genital activity which is more satisfactory than productive of anxiety. One might think that the puberty change at least is something inevitably fixed and impervious to cultural influence. According to Sullivan, it may be considerably delayed.

In any case, in early adolescence there is a very rapid en-

[52] These include a series of models, familiarity with whom is necessary in order to profit from trial-and-error learning as one progresses toward becoming fully human.

[53] "Towards a Psychiatry of Peoples," *Psychiatry,* Vol. 11, No. 2, May, 1948, p. 108.

hancement of interest in developing techniques for contact with a member of the other sex. It becomes necessary to get to know and learn to live with and respect a member of the other sex. So the thing, in Sullivan's view, especially characteristic of this period is not maturation of the genital lust dynamism but the shift in the need for intimacy from a representative of one's own sex to a member of the other sex, though adolescence is "ushered in" by both. Please note that it is not merely a matter of so-called libidinal development.

Each one of those two "components" can "collide" with, can, under certain circumstances, threaten other things which became important to one in his previous development. Needless to say, in our society, lust often collides with the need for security and if certain unfortunate experiences occurred in early life lust may be dissociated. Also there can be and sometimes there is a collision between the need for security, that is freedom from anxiety, and the achievement of self-respect, and the shift in the intimacy need as, for instance, where a parent is unwilling to allow a youth to grow up, emancipate himself from the parents, find a mate, etc. The parent may disparage or ridicule his efforts at emancipation. In our society, collisions of lust and the intimacy need itself are perhaps very frequent, a condition marked by diffidence, excessive precautions or of excessive boldness. Collisions of lust and the intimacy need may result in various misfortunes accompanying or following the initial sexual act: impotence, a revulsion toward sex, etc.

Three outstanding attitudes toward lust, toward sex may be distinguished. First, that it is "a great thing." Second, that it is a menace and exposes one to dreadful humiliations. Third, that active cooperation in sex is not merely a source of insecurity, but that the feeling of lust or even revery processes "colored" by lust are experienced as a profound depreciation of one's self-esteem. As Sullivan expressed this third possibility, it is "disgraceful, disgusting and damned."

In regard to the patterning of sexual behavior, Sullivan claimed there were dozens of reasonably probable patterns of sexual behavior. But I shall not strain your mathematical powers by discussing them. Instead I shall discuss a few things psychiatrically significant regarding early adolescence. Both the need for intimacy with the other sex and lust can be disintegrated and integrated into other patterns of behavior. For example, regarding the intimacy need, it may be disintegrated and sublimated (reintegrated)[54] in such a fashion that the person's relationships are very like that of a boy's relation to his sister or a girl's to her brother. Other possibilities in such cases are: placing women on an unreachable pedestal ("ennoblement of women") if one is a boy, an unutterable devotion to a member of the other sex who is well advanced beyond early adolescence, a spurious "hating" of the other sex, etc. Disintegration of lust is said to be transient, dangerously unstable, and if the process is prolonged, almost certain to lead to a very serious upheaval of personality.

The need for intimacy with a member of the other sex can be dissociated. Such a person, because of a lot of unnoted "come-on," may find himself always getting into awkward, unexpected, embarrassing and anxiety-provoking situations.[55] Lust also can be dissociated, in part better than entire. But dissociation of lust is said to be always risky. There are of course many more complexities involved in these matters which one cannot briefly discuss.

Loneliness is the experience connected with the inadequate fulfillment of the need for interpersonal intimacy. In adolescence this need is carried over, or expanded into, a need for intimacy with a member of the other sex. The manifestations of this need may be classified under three heads: the heterophilic, where the person is intensely interested in achieving intimacy with a member (or members) of the other sex; the isophilic, where the person has, *in this respect*, not progressed beyond preadolescence, and regards only members of his own sex as suitable for intimacy; and the autophilic, where either there has been no preadolescent development, or, owing to unfortunate experience, such as painful, thwarting rebuff, the person has "returned" to a pre-preadolescent state, where his "love," if it exists at all, is concen-

[54] Sullivan also says that instead of sublimation a "regressive reappearance" of earlier patterns of behavior may occur.

[55] If this sort of thing persists, Sullivan says, in a man, it leads to the "true" woman hater who gradually gets to feel that women are a menace.

trated "within" his personification of himself, which, by a very free interpretation of one of Freud's doctrines, might be called narcissism.

Perhaps I can guard against confusion of what I have just been saying about the intimacy need with lustful (sexual) behavior or lustful desires when one is referring to a person's orientation in living by calling attention to the fact that the intimacy need and lust are two *distinct* integrating tendencies. The lust dynamism has to be understood separately, and under two classifications: (1) on the basis of preferred partner (or substitute) and (2) on the basis of genital participation or substitution.

I believe much of what I said is summed up in the following sentence: a person's orientation in living "is derived from consensually validated trial-and-error learning from personal examples, analysis and synthesis of the experience thus obtained, and the remedial disintegration of self-system processes which have survived from the earlier 'education by anxiety'" [56] . . . By orientation in living is meant a formulated or relatively easily formulable grasp of or into "the integrating tendencies customarily characterizing one's interpersonal relations, the circumstances appropriate to their satisfactory and relatively anxiety-free discharge, and the more or less remote goals for the approximation of which one will forego intercurrent opportunities for satisfaction or the enhancement of one's prestige." [57] This is what one means by a well-integrated personality. To the degree that one approximates those conditions, to that degree one is well-integrated.

Sullivan's theories of personality development appear to have been formulated primarily in order to help him understand mental disorder and assist "therapeutic operations." But I cannot undertake to explain briefly how he "used" his theories of personality development for psychiatric purposes without risk of being seriously inaccurate or of being misunderstood. However,

[56] Quoted from an unpublished lecture by permission of the William Alanson White Psychiatric Foundation. See copyright page.

[57] Quoted from an unpublished lecture by permission of William Alanson White Psychiatric Foundation. See copyright page.

I may mention one or two things. He claimed that, barring subsequent fortunate experience having remedial effects, the earlier in developmental history a "deviation" or "distortion" occurs, the more extensive its influence on the subsequent development of interpersonal relations. And he did not believe that a close correlation could be found between "types" of mental disorder and a given time in the developmental evolution of personality. He also rejected the Freudian notion of a causal trauma as too static. This is not surprising if only because of his extremely dynamic conception of psychology.

Although he spoke of an arrest of development at this or that era, his formulation of it does not imply that at any one point a person's experience becomes "static" in the sense that it is the same old thing from then on, or a mechanical repetition. Arrest and deviation of development occur in the sense that there is delay in the statistically "usual" course of events and that, later, "eccentricities" and "distortions" in interpersonal relations are manifested. *Some* experience necessary for successful living may be missed, and some may be "distorted."

Others will discuss the more technically psychiatric side of Sullivan's theories and techniques. I want to observe only that toward the traditional neat rigid classifications of mental disorder he heaped ridicule and biting criticism. They were, he claimed, often a means of saving one the trouble of having to do some laborious thinking and painstaking research. He thought that many of the differences that are alleged to be verifiable are at best capable of only vague definition though it would be preposterous, he admitted, to say that psychiatrists refer to nothing when they diagnose a person as schizophrenic. For him everything that is found in mentally disordered people is found in everyone else—only the accent, the prominence, the misuse of certain things is said to be more characteristic of the former. As he liked to say, we are all much more simply human than otherwise.

One must realize that Sullivan was first and last a clinical psychiatrist. All or nearly all his theories and techniques were evolved for the purpose of facilitating therapeutic work. Regarding therapy, he said, useful "psychiatric interpretations essen-

Concept = operations

tially are statements of preferably alternative hypotheses *which in every case are to be scrutinized further.*[58] He was hostile to broad generalizations which may sound grand but leave patient and psychiatrist just where they were if used as interpretive principles. And the fact that his theories at least in broad outline have received considerable support from social psychologists, anthropologists and sociologists seems a good omen for the future of those theories. The next most important step will be, I surmise, a more rigorous integration of interpersonal theory with sociology.[59]

In recent years following the lead of the philosophers Charles Peirce, William James, John Dewey, the physicist P. W. Bridgman, and others, Sullivan advocated "operationism" in psychiatry. To be sure his approach to psychiatry for a long time had been "operationalist" in a wide sense. But, I think, only in late years, not long before his death, did he become self-consciously operationalist, due in part, I surmise, to the reckless manner in which terms and ideas have been manipulated in psychiatry.

Now, operationism has its shortcomings too, I believe, if narrowly understood, but I cannot go into that because it would take me far away from the main issues of this paper. In his *The Logic of Modern Physics,*[60] Bridgman introduced an approach according to which a concept or idea is identical with the set of operations by which it is applied. I shall state this in Bridgman's own words: "In general we mean by any concept nothing more than a set of operations; *the concept is synonymous with the corresponding set of operations.*" [61] Hence the "proper definition" of a concept is said to be in terms of actual operations. What, for example, does the concept of length mean? The answer is located in the fact that in order to find the length of an object,

[58] "Therapeutic Investigations in Schizophrenia" in *A Study of Interpersonal Relations,* p. 449, edited by Patrick Mullahy, Hermitage Press, Inc., New York, 1949.

[59] Compare *The Human Group* by George C. Homans, Harcourt, Brace and Co., New York, 1950. See also the important paper by Arnold W. Green, "Duplicity," in *Psychiatry,* 6:411, p. 424.

[60] The Macmillan Co., New York, 1927.

[61] Op. cit., p. 5.

we must perform certain physical operations. "The concept of
length," Bridgman says, "is therefore fixed when the operations
by which length is measured are fixed: that is, the concept of
length involves as much as and nothing more than a set of operations by which length is determined." [62] Bridgman (and others)
believe that the true meaning of a term is to be discovered by
observing what one does with it, not what one says about it.[63]
In one of his unpublished lectures Sullivan quotes some of
Bridgman's statements from his paper on "Operationism" published in the *Psychological Review* (1945). Bridgman says: [64]

> "A term is defined when the conditions are stated
> under which I may use the term, and when I may infer
> from the use of the term by my neighbor that the same
> conditions prevailed."

Bridgman goes on to say that one of the most important presuppositions of scientific enterprise is the possibility of checking
or verifying the correctness of any statement—that checking to
see the conditions are satisfied is accomplished by performing
certain operations so that for all essential purposes a definition
may be specified in terms of the checking operations.

Sullivan strove hard to achieve at least an approximation of
such scientific presuppositions even though his subject-matter
does not readily lend itself to precise statements.

Perhaps I can indicate the importance of precise definitions
by mentioning the vagueness and ambiguity of the Freudian term
identification. I shall not go into the various ramifications of
Freud's use of this idea, though I hope some day some one will
make a study of the number of *different* senses in which Freud
and his followers use it. Here I shall limit myself to a few illustrations of its vagueness and ambiguity. In the *New Introductory
Lectures* (pp. 90-91) Freud says that in what is called an identification "one ego becomes like another, one which results in

[62] Op. cit., p. 5.

[63] Op. cit., p. 7. Compare *Knowing and The Known*, by John Dewey
and Arthur F. Bentley, The Beacon Press, Boston, 1949, p. 210 f.

[64] "Some Principles of Operational Analysis," Vol. 52, p. 246.

Concept ascribed

the first ego behaving itself in certain respects in the same way
as the second; it imitates it, and as it were takes it into itself." [65]
Such a statement is vague, to say the least, but the next sentence
might well drive a logician to despair, for Freud says that identification has not been "inappropriately compared with the oral
cannibalistic incorporation of another person." Nor is this all
there is to it. Freud goes on to warn the reader not to confuse
identification with object-choice. In the former case if a boy
identifies himself with the father, he wishes to be *like* him. And
when he makes his father his object-choice, he wishes to *have*
him, he wishes to possess him. In identification the boy's ego
"is altered on the model of his father." This is not necessary in
the second case. And there are still further ramifications to
Freud's concept of identification.

His explanation is vague enough, but some of his followers
have not helped much in this respect. Dr. Daniel E. Schneider in
The Psychoanalyst and the Artist (pp. 16-17)[66] discussing the
reactions of an audience to a play says when we identify, "we
do not 'pattern ourselves after' a model; we *become* him [the
actor as 'blended' into his role], his attitude, his voice, his creative intelligence *as all these things erupt and reverberate, in
waves and echoes, against the furthermost boundaries and with
the penetrating implications of the other characterizations which,
in dynamic relation to him, comprise the situation and give it
form.*" And we identify with the traditions and ideals of the character, that is, with his super-ego. We also "take over" a portion
of his id., etc. Furthermore, Dr. Schneider, shortly before this,
tells us when we identify in such dramatic situations, we, among
other things, "*project* ourselves into the setting and own the
furniture."

Let us examine one more instance, namely, Dr. Gregory
Zilboorg's statements about identification. In his *Sigmund Freud*
(p. 97)[67] he first quotes Freud regarding identification: "Everything that establishes common interests among people calls upon
the formation of feelings in common, upon our ability to develop

[65] W. W. Norton & Co., Inc., New York, 1933.
[66] Farrar, Straus and Co., New York, 1950.
[67] Charles Scribner's Sons, New York, 1951.

identifications with one another." What Freud has in mind "of course," says Dr. Zilboorg—though I shall not inquire as to how he has this wonderful capacity to *know* just what went on in Freud's mind, especially since quite a number of different things seem to have gone on in Freud's mind regarding identification judging from his statements about it—"is our true ability to put ourselves in the place of others, automatically as it were . . ." And Dr. Zilboorg adds, "As Freud himself could have said, the conscious, purely intellectual, calculated and calculating manner of 'imagining' the position of our neighbor may lead, not to identification, but to the reading into our neighbor of our own reactions—which would mean a *projection*. An identification means an emotional, a *feeling* identification—an actual feeling as if you were the other person."

One might ask Dr. Zilboorg how one can put oneself in the place of another "automatically as it were." Or just what "an actual feeling as if you were the other person" means.

I could go on indefinitely to give examples of the reckless fashion in which terms and ideas are manipulated by the disciples of *various* "schools" of psychiatry, but instead I want to emphasize the fact that there is no chance that psychiatry will ever be a truly scientific field of inquiry until, as a first step toward scientific progress, it adopts a language sufficiently precise that its practitioners as well as other workers in allied and related fields can in various ways check and verify the correctness of statements made by one another.[68]

I am aware that Sullivan's advocacy of operationism has extremely radical implications for psychiatric theory and practice. If wisely "handled," it might advance psychiatry to a position where psychiatrists might well be truly cooperative workers in the study of man. It would facilitate a close cooperation with social scientists and with all students of science. Therefore it would facilitate and enhance the achievement of a science of man.

Because of his untimely death, Sullivan did not have an op-

[68] Compare Morris R. Cohen and Ernest Nagel in *An Introduction to Logic and Scientific Method*, pp. 191-403, Harcourt, Brace and Co., New York, 1934, particularly with reference to the role of hypotheses.

portunity to carry through his program in a comprehensive fashion. And so the task largely remains for those students of psychiatry and psychology who have, like Sullivan and Freud, courage and an unremitting determination in the face of obstacles.

Hand in hand with operationism I suggest should go what Robert K. Merton calls "conceptual analysis" (though he of course is thinking in terms of sociological theory and research). Our "conceptual language," he observes, "tends to fix our perceptions and, derivatively, our thought and behavior. The concept defines the situation, and the research worker responds accordingly. Explicit conceptual analysis helps him recognize to what he is responding and which (possibly significant) elements he is ignoring." [69] As everyone knows, in psychiatry there is a plenitude of different "schools," each operating with a different "orientation" and each, or rather the adherents of each, responding to a different conceptualized situation.

While it would be naive to imagine that such things as operationism and conceptual analysis will automatically rule out institutional biases in psychiatry, or solve various problems which interpersonal theory in psychiatry is faced with, I surmise they can be a considerable aid in its further progress if intelligently and sincerely applied.[70]

[69] *Social Theory and Social Structure*, pp. 87-90. His discussion of *post factum* explanations (pp. 90-91) seems to me equally relevant to psychiatry.

[70] This paper was not presented in its entirety at the symposium due to the fact that much preliminary work had already been done on this discussion of Sullivan's theories before I suggested to Dr. Joseph S. Miller that such a symposium on Sullivan be held. For obvious reasons, it has seemed advisable to publish this paper without deletions.

CHAPTER II

*SULLIVAN'S CONCEPTIONS**

ALFRED H. STANTON
Cushing V. A. Hospital

A DISCUSSION of Sullivan's second series of lectures on the conceptions of modern psychiatry, from the point of view of a clinician, is at first glance an impractical assignment. This group of thirty-four lectures, given several times, is so well integrated that, even though many of the conceptions are phrased in ways which are strange to the language of clinical psychiatry, the clinical parts can be separated from the non-clinical parts only arbitrarily. They show in their structure that they arose from clinical practice of psychotherapy, that is, the study of interpersonal relations by participant observation with patients.

The place of this second Conceptions of Modern Psychiatry in Sullivan's life illustrates in another way the degree to which they were clinically oriented. They were lectures used to teach, in schools of psychiatry in Washington and New York, workers who were in general actively engaged in various kinds of therapeutically intended human relations. The teaching was done at great personal cost, for Dr. Sullivan was not well during many

---

* I have inserted most of the words and phrases in brackets in order to make the quotations more intelligible. A few insertions were made by Dr. Stanton.—The Editor.

of the times that this second series was given. The urgency with which he ignored his own ill-health in order to prepare and give these lectures, as a way of helping students to "organize thought" about interpersonal relations, suggests a constant awareness on his part of therapeutic needs.

There is still a different way in which the lectures betray their general clinical origin. After his death, it was the author's privilege to have the opportunity, at least hurriedly, to survey the unpublished, as well as the published, works of Dr. Sullivan. As most of you know, during the first decade of his clinical life, his papers were highly empirical, and though critical, used the general framework of thought of the time. They were, in general, discussions of some particular point about schizophrenic processes arising from his work at Sheppard and Enoch Pratt Hospital. This interest expanded to include the structure of the psychiatric ward as a whole and, for a time, he organized and carried on a ward specifically for the purpose of treating young, male, first-attack schizophrenic patients. At about the same time, he came in close contact with Edward Sapir and a quite remarkable convergence of their views occurred in a major insight that psychiatry might well be recognized as, in fact, study of interpersonal relations. There followed a pronounced change in the character of his papers during the next decade, beginning with the publication of his paper on Socio-Psychiatric Research,[1] which illustrated the new point of view. In this decade, the 1930's, during which he studied patients in the obsessional-schizoid group particularly, he was developing the implications of this particular insight which led up to his first *Conceptions of Modern Psychiatry* in 1940. He repeatedly expressed much dissatisfaction with this first "Conceptions" but after ten more years he had developed his point of view so much more fully that he was able to express his general satisfaction with the major formulations which appear in the second "Conceptions." Transcriptions of many of these lectures were fortunately made and they

[1] The paper is entitled *Socio-Psychiatric Research: Its Implications for the Schizophrenic Problem and for Mental Hygiene,* which appeared in the AMERICAN JOURNAL OF PSYCHIATRY in 1932 (10:977-991).—The Editor.

are now well under way in their somewhat tortuous route toward publication.

We will try to clarify here the clinical importance of this view of Dr. Sullivan's that psychiatry is the study of interpersonal relations in the light of the second "Conceptions." Just how much difference, and what difference, can it make to the practitioner that this insight came to Dr. Sullivan and that he developed it as he did?

It is worth while to make explicit certain aspects of the clinician's point of view in making use of conceptions such as those of Dr. Sullivan. The clinician has a very great asset in that he often earns his living, literally, in psychotherapy, a social situation where he is expected to help in bringing about change. This demand for change protects him from believing that sterile theorizing makes any particular difference. It is perfectly clear now that theorizing itself does not bring about change in any reliable way in the manifestations of mental disorder. His daily work then tends to favor a lasting and high motivation for both receptivity to new conceptions and to a discriminating and practically-based criticism of them. If theory is irrelevant, *or is not grasped by the psychiatrist,* it makes no difference; if on the other hand it opens his eyes to new avenues of inquiry into important matters it becomes a part of him. It must be confessed, however, that the clinical situation also brings with it considerable temptation toward a rough and ready eclectic pseudo-empiricism, perhaps better called opportunism, which may present considerable barriers to clear, careful and persistent thought. The clinical life also brings with it serious problems of professional and organizational loyalties, and particularly urgent problems of prestige and professional reputation. When one remembers that, in addition, clinicians keep themselves exceedingly busy, it is not surprising that very little of the rich store of intuitive wisdom rising out of clinical experience makes its way into psychiatric technical literature in a generally usable way. Dr. Sullivan's work is an exception to this. His theory was part of his practice.

These introductory thoughts may throw light on one of the characteristics of Dr. Sullivan's Conceptions—his special lan-

guage. His language is quite strikingly different from that which
is usual in clinical psychiatry. This was unavoidable, a result
primarily of the originality of his observations and his determination not to have his ideas lost in a morass of conventional
ambiguities. It will be useful to quote from one of his notebooks.
These notebooks, while written primarily for himself, are so
clearly organized that they are easily understandable in the form
he set them down.[2] "Any scientific discipline has to use a special
language. Psychiatry, perhaps long before it could aspire to the
rank of a full-fledged scientific discipline, became possessed with
a great deal of special language. Two of many reasons for this
fact may be mentioned: (1) Psychiatry as science deals with the
most complex of all fields of knowledge—this in itself explains
why psychiatric knowledge lags behind studies of infra-human
nature; (2) The practical problem of dealing with people, regarded as the primary concern of psychiatrists, has never been
easy, nor the results particularly gratifying to anyone. It has
seemed important, therefore, if one is committed to such a calling, to make up with language operations, addressed to critics, for
one's inability to demonstrate one's work by material achievement.

"The basic position in the present undertaking may be stated
as follows:

"Psychiatry, properly defined, is a science, a fundamental
division of knowledge. Psychiatry is fully entitled to a special
referential language.

"Since psychiatry, as defined, is a science dealing with operational conceptions, its special, referential language may well be
derived from typical interpersonal action which, from the nature of personality, must be identified with the common reportory
language of the people concerned—which language, however,
insofar as it is made the special language of psychiatry, *ceases*
to be common speech and open to any damned interpretations
which appeal to the hearers; insofar as he [that is, the psychia-

---

[2] The quotations in this lecture were taken from unpublished transcriptions of Sullivan's lectures and from an unpublished notebook of his and
used here by permission of the William Alanson White Psychiatric Foundation. See copyright page.

trist] is a student of psychiatry, he has to learn the precise meaning of its terms."

Dr. Sullivan regarded the individual organism as the subject of study of psychobiology. He regarded the social heritage showing in the concerted behavior of persons making up a group as the subject of study in cultural anthropology. In contrast, he thought that "the biologically and culturally conditioned, but *sui generis,* interpersonal processes occurring in interpersonal situations is the subject for study in psychiatry." [3] It will be noted that he did *not* regard psychiatry as the study of personality or of mental illness. As far as personality was concerned, he stated, "It is conventional to say that experience is personal, but for scientific psychiatry, personality has to be relegated to the realm of hypothetical entities, factually to account for dynamic characteristics of interpersonal relations." [4]

The relative unfamiliarity of Dr. Sullivan's language, then, can be explained in part by the fact that he took very great precautions *not* to say some of the things that are rattled off conventionally by psychiatrists. We have already emphasized the fact that for him psychiatry was a study of interpersonal relations, not of personality or of the organism. He rarely used such terms as "mind," "individual," "environment," or "reality," unless he used them in quotation marks. For instance, the term "mind" implies, as frequently used, that it exists somehow separate and distinct from, set over against, the environment or the rest of the organism. This fringe of meaning he succeeded in avoiding. If one chooses to study what he wrote rather than merely to browse in it, his careful avoidance of many such implications pays dividends. For instance, another common set of tacit assumptions— that social relations or interpersonal relations are relatively "superficial," "obvious," easy to describe and easy to understand, that all one needs is to be "objective" and to understand reality—can hardly survive if one reads Sullivan carefully. It is clear that a significant part of Dr. Sullivan's effort (and he worked very hard) arose precisely because of his efforts to avoid these com-

[3] This quotation from Sullivan is taken from unpublished material. See copyright page.

[4] From Sullivan's unpublished papers. See copyright page.

mon, tacit assumptions which are imbedded in our technical language. It required much ingenuity not to build these assumptions into a theory which he wanted to develop rigorously and thoroughly.

It would be well, however, to illustrate in Dr. Sullivan's own words the difference between the special field of interpersonal relations and the psychobiological. You will recall his concept of euphoria, approximated originally in the human animal shortly after birth, as a state of relaxation and the relative inactivity of deep sleep. This euphoria is interrupted by recurrent disturbing tensions which are relieved by specific patterns of activity, leading to relaxation of the tensions, that is to satisfaction. These tensions, to which he also referred as needs, are differentiated in the experience of the infant by the precise activity which leads to their relaxation. The needs derive their meaning from this activity. Such tensions, then, are directional. The whole pattern he considered as a unit, calling it a dynamism.

But this "human animal," the infant, who experiences these recurrent tensions and the patterns leading to their relaxation, this organism as it occurs in nature, has these needs met, in general, through the agency of a person—the mothering one. This social situation is equally real, equally a part of the phenomena comprising the child's living, as are the physico-chemical processes and the tensions and activities leading to their relief. Sullivan summarized the life-saving aspect of this interpersonal relation by what he called his "theorem of tenderness." "The observed activity of the infant arising from the tension of needs, induces tension in the mothering one, which tension is experienced as tenderness, an impulsion to activities toward the relief of the infant's needs.

"This in a way is a definition of tenderness, a very important conception, very different from the miscellaneous and in general meaningless term 'love' which confuses so many issues in our current day and age.

"The manifest activity toward the relief of the infant's needs will presently be experienced by the infant as the undergoing of tender behavior, as needs for the relaxation of which the co-operation of another is required . . .

"When we speak of a generic need for tenderness—even though the needs that are included are direct derivatives of disequilibrium arising from the physical-chemical universe—nonetheless since these generic needs all require cooperation from another, [we say] the need for tenderness is ingrained from the very beginning of things as an interpersonal need." [5] Here is an explicit statement of the relation between an interpersonal need as discriminated from needs arising from physical-chemical change.

Besides the need for tenderness Sullivan emphasized another interpersonal fact observable in infancy, summarized in his theorem of anxiety: "The tension of anxiety when present in the mothering one induces anxiety in the infant." This clearly interpersonal process acts generally in opposition to the satisfaction of needs, that is, of other tensions. It is important to emphasize that the child's anxiety occurs when the mother is anxious and that the mother's anxiety may or may not be simply related to what is happening between her and the infant. Her anxiety may have been provoked by difficulties with the grocer. In any case, the times when the mother becomes anxious are for the child completely arbitrary, but nevertheless impose on *him* the necessity of developing ways to diminish the tension. The effective ways of reducing anxiety early in life will of necessity be related closely to the personality of the mothering one, to those events which lead to a diminution of her anxiety. The infant then develops recurrent patterns of activities whose result is merely the reduction of anxiety in ways dictated by the mother's personality organization; the absolutely arbitrary rote learning by the focusing of attention upon this problem of avoiding or minimizing anxiety leads to the development of what Sullivan calls the *self-dynamism*, a dynamism which is purely interpersonal in origin. Later these activities are personified as "I" and "Me," as "good me" and "bad me," and in cases where very severe anxiety has been encountered as "not me." But again it is important to emphasize that if Sullivan's theory is followed, this self-system and these personifications could no more exist without another

[5] This quotation from Sullivan is taken from unpublished material. See copyright page.

person than could language. The personified self is in effect a group of reflected appraisals—though it is not, of course, naively sensed as such. Many patients speak of their "real" self, the "core" of their personality or in similar terms. For Sullivan, the "real self" is a personification of processes whose form was first developed in interaction with the mothering one.

As the child matures, his activity leading to the reduction of anxiety becomes more and more effective, and he comes to be able to foresee anxiety and to avoid it. The graded induction of anxiety becomes an important part of the process of acculturation of the child. The self-system becomes highly organized and relatively resistant to change, and more independent of the anxiety of the person directly before one. The self-system, like the need for tenderness, arises in, takes its form from, manifests itself in and only in, interaction with other persons; at first these persons are real, later they may be real or illusory, or to use Sullivan's phrase "eidetic."

What is the condition of the person when he reaches adulthood? What are the manifestations of these processes in the usual clinical setting? What relation do they bear to mental disorder? It is not surprising that for Sullivan the conception of mental disorder is again an original one; a strictly interpersonal consideration of mental disorder would have to be different from usual ideas. It will be well to quote at some length in an attempt to grasp his interpersonal definition of "mental" disorder.

"If any dynamism is called into action, whether by such things as biochemical necessities so that one gets hungry, or an attractive and seductive looking person, whereupon one gets lustful . . . there are three major states that will ensue. There will be tension which is equivalent to need, or the felt component of any dynamism's activity, and covert and overt processes, and in many cases, uncomplicated cases, the activity which is called out in the people involved . . . will satisfy the need—or [that is, will] resolve the situation which has been integrated by the dynamism. Now, if satisfaction is not readily obtained, there will be a continuation of the tension and perhaps accentuated covert and overt processes looking to the resolution of the situation. But sometimes the development of the situation is such that the possibility of any easy resolution of the situation, any reasonably prompt satisfaction of need or elevation of self is flatly contradicted by elements in the situation . . . elements which may be the motivational system of another, or which may be something else. And in that case one of three outcomes is probable.

"In the first, and the one which is perhaps most common in frustrating situations, there is an increase in tension, and the appearance of supplementary processes of various kinds. In a less common outcome, more in keeping with recurrent frustration, with very severe humiliation and so on mixed in with the frustration, the integrating tendency, [which is part of] the self-dynamism, is disintegrated and reconstituted, or is dissociated from easy access to awareness and operates after the fashion of a dissociated system as I have described. Now if one realizes that this sort of consideration applies to any dynamism which is related to any interpersonal situation . . . then it will be a little easier to follow some of the development which I will offer, starting out with what I can entitle 'The Classification of Mental Disorders.' But I would suggest that you put single quotation marks around 'mental disorders' because the idea of mental disorder to be discussed here may not be quite the idea you have.

". . . One of the very common instances in which this continuation of tension puts in appearance is where the activation of a superior dynamism is complicated by the activation of a less potent dynamism, the satisfaction of which is not congruent with the processes already in the picture." [6]

Two different types of collision of dynamisms are apt to exist. If there is merely the collision of two dynamisms, neither of which is threatening to the self-system, distraction, suppression, or a combination of both occurs. But if anxiety is involved, other processes are noticeable.

"One is where the protection of self-esteem, the avoidance of anxiety, is the process manifesting the superior dynamism, and the secondary activity is one that would collide with the protection or maintenance of self-esteem. Now when that happens,

[6] This quotation from Sullivan is taken from unpublished material. See copyright page.

we can be sure that the activity of the second dynamism is attended by the experience of at least a trace of anxiety, a hint of anxiety, if you please. And what with amazing frequency follows this hint is the manifestation of the process which we call *selective inattention.* If that does not occur, or if it doesn't suffice, then some other supplementary process is called out.

"Let me take a very commonplace instance which has happened to all of you. Let us say that two people are having a technical discussion and that later in this discussion one of them recalls very vividly something that the other had said and sees what it means, which he had not noticed at all before. He now, apropos of something or other, sees the relevant implications of the earlier statement by which, at the time of its utterance, he had been only very slightly distracted. In other words, the initial utterance of this significant statement disturbed the processes of his mind momentarily, but it was clearly recorded because when it became particularly significant, it reappears as the statement with its implications.

"In contrast let us consider the case where the significant remark causes slight distraction, but at no subsequent time is recalled . . . Nor is there any subsequent development of its implications . . . It is often to be assumed—if the remark and its implications were of importance to the exchange—that the slight distraction was of that peculiar kind which we call a hint of anxiety. This sort of thing—where something obviously happened but there is no subsequent evidence that anything happened—is a particular instance of the almost ubiquitous process which we call selective inattention.

"This [selective inattention] is an activity of the self-system to deny awareness to something which is anxiety fraught, incongruent with the tendencies incorporated in the self-system; in other words, it is one of an infinite number of instances of how the self-system tends to maintain itself against, you might say, experience which should bring about change. And this selective inattention can be said to be about the commonest of those things that we call mental disorders. Now if any of you have an idea that mental disorder ought to apply to things awful and terrible, I trust this has cured that idea. Mental disorder, like the poor, is everywhere. It can be severe, it's often so mild and conventional that we don't think of it as anything but living." [7]

It may be helpful to pause here. If one follows usual lines of thought, one notes here that selective inattention can perhaps be called a mental disorder because it is an inadequacy of a sort in the mind of one person. Sullivan's development is significantly different from this.

"The person in our discussion whose remark has been ignored may think, as he puts it, that his partner in the discussion is not paying attention at the time. Or that he did not know enough to follow that particular statement. If these thoughts are followed by exploration, if he repeats the statement, for example, he is apt to be convinced that it is a case of stupidity, and not an instance of not paying attention—for the repetition he made is no more effective than was the first statement. This conclusion of our discussant about his companion's inattention is not an adequate explanation of the event. *And to the extent that it is not an adequate explanation, but is nevertheless entertained, it complicates the interpersonal situation.* [Italics by H. S. Stanton.] Now that which complicates makes things complex. And so whatever you had thought complex means, here is a hint—it means that which has been complicated.

"I hope you can see without my harping on it, why neither the idea that his friend was not paying attention, nor the idea that his friend was too stupid to follow the proposition, is correct. Neither has any reference to the intervention of anxiety and the self-system, and therefore they are beside the point . . . The inadequate explanation which our discussant had for the selective inattention of his friend was a derogatory estimation of his friend's mentality, which is a disjunctive process. So . . . it was not solely the person who showed selective inattention who complicated the situation. *It was also* [italics by A. H. Stanton] the person who introduced the gratuitous derogatory estimation, which further reduced or impaired the adequacy of the integration of the two necessary for the discussion.

"If in addition to the two hypotheses, the discussant had been

[7] This quotation from Sullivan is taken from unpublished material. See copyright page.

able to entertain a third one, namely, that the ignored statement was disturbing to the person who did not attend to it, then he would have approximated correctness in our particular instance and could have explored the probability of the third hypothesis and gotten evidence which strongly encouraged belief in its probability. In that case he would have done something which would aid in obtaining the most that could be obtained from the discussion under the circumstances where a part of the discussion made one party anxious." [8]

In contrast to mental disorder—the complicating of interpersonal situations—Sullivan found it possible to describe the opposite—"simple" interpersonal relations. Interpersonal relations are simple, first, if the motivations concerned involve no other parataxically concomitant or fantastically illusory people, unreal people, if you like that very slippery word; second, if no components of the motivation are suppressed or discharged in some other situation such as sleep; and, third, if integration of the situation is not impaired or destroyed by the occurrence of disjunctive processes before it has been resolved. Such "simple" situations may last for long periods of time, and involve many activities, but in Sullivan's sense remain "simple"—if they do not involve illusory people or the discharge of motivation elsewhere, and if they proceed without interruption to satisfactory resolution. Simple situations work. Here is his definition of health. Such simple situations, and the complicated ones which are mental disorder, both involve two or more people, and ordinarily, both are constructions built and maintained by two or more people. And complicated ones do not work as well.

What can be done by the practicing psychiatrist in dealing with complicated interpersonal situations? Let us follow farther.

"Now I wish to discuss how we propose to handle what I choose to call selective inattention—that is, what may be in the mind in the particular observer of a situation characterized by the occurrence of selective inattention. I shall first talk about what may be called participant observation of selective inattention as it affects or appears in the patient.

8 This quotation from Sullivan is taken from unpublished material. See copyright page.

"The participant observation of *selective* inattention . . . is primarily a matter of validating an hypothesis or series of hypotheses. In our particular instance of the discussion we have considered three hypotheses which were reasonable to entertain, except that for a doctor it is not reasonable to entertain a derogatory view of a patient as stupid. But there are several variants which might be worth our while.

"Let us talk about the situation and then the hypothesis. Some remark, or comment, or question, or what not, fails to provoke, to call out, any overt element of its interpersonal occurrence.

"Next the physician and his hypotheses. The first is that the patient was inattentive, simply inattentively occupied, or what have you, and did not hear; the second, that the patient did not understand the comment, and for some reason did not seek to find out what was meant; and the third, that it is an instance of selective inattention—that is, the comment called out some anxiety and its purport was denied access to awareness.

"If you will look at hypothesis two—that the patient did not understand the comment and for some reason did not seek to find out what it meant—you will observe that there will be several [possible] reasons besides anxiety for not asking. Also [you will note], that anxiety may be present and effective in *wittingly* ignoring the comment which was anxiety-fraught—which is not an instance of selective inattention. In other words, these three are by no means all the hypotheses that are perfectly plausible for you to entertain in seeking an understanding of an instance of selective inattention, which is not labeled. God sends you no power [of justifiably] saying [or immediately knowing] that this is selective inattention. We observe that it could be at least four or five things, including selective inattention, and that all these hypotheses of what the event means are plausible and in need of testing.

"Unless more than the first hypothesis has occurred to the psychiatrist, he will probably repeat the comment that was ignored immediately, and this may be all right in case the first hypothesis was correct: namely, the hypothesis that the patient, thinking about his income tax, or something, had not heard the psychiatrist. But *if it is anything but the first* [italics by A. H. Stanton], it will not be all right because an immediate repetition of a comment that has caused anxiety, [and] has been selectively ignored, will cause more anxiety and a very decided disturbance of the communication situation. The first hypothesis is a reasonable basis for immediate testing only if other circumstances have been noted which indicate the probability of simple inattention; if, for example, there was a backfire in the streets the same time as you were mouthing your important comments, it is quite possible that the patient heard the backfire and not your remark. In which case hypothesis one is all right and it is perfectly reasonable to repeat your comment and see what happens. But, unless there is some tight, plausible reason to suppose that it's that simple, skill would suggest that one does not immediately crash a situation by presenting the same comment again.

"Hypothesis two—that the patient didn't understand and for some reason didn't answer—may become highly plausible when one recalls the form of one's comment. In this case, where one sees that one has made one's comment in a fashion that might fail to communicate meaning to the hearer, then one notices this and plans presently to make the remark, or ask the question in different words but without material change of its import and particularly not in an incongruous context. There is a general principle [I want to mention] that unless a patient and his physician proceed in a *somewhat* [italics by A. H. Stanton] comprehensible way to converse with one another, no one, including God, can know what's being discussed. We don't wait until we are in the midst of something else and then spring something dreadfully irrelevant to see whether it was misunderstood before—it would certainly be misunderstood this time and prove nothing except that it is hard to follow the psychiatrist. Well, if on this repetition the patient shows obvious embarrassment, one has to account for a witting avoidance of the import of the comment, which is not selective inattention.

"If, however, when we get our repetition [effected] in different words, [and] again nothing shows that the purport has reached the patient, then and only then it becomes quite probable that you are dealing with an instance of selective inattention. At this point, from the nature of selective inattention, it is ordinarily advisable to note the probability for subsequent exploration. "Subsequent" will mean later in the course of the relationship whenever it is reasonably certain there will be more than one contact. Sometimes it *may* be advisable to do something about selective inattention in the first interview. And what one does about it where one is going after it hammer and tongs in this fashion is what I like to call direct validation. One refers specifically to the patient's inattention to the particular remark or comment or question and sees what happens. If that which is dealt with is selective inattention, is anxiety-fraught, what will happen will be either a security operation to reduce, to minimize the anxiety, or it will be severe anxiety. In the former case one may secure useful data on the patient's personified self. In the latter event, the [occurrence of] severe anxiety, one has brought oneself the task of handling the anxiety in a way that will conserve the doctor-patient relationship. Otherwise the patient may believe on the way home (the lucid interval after he has escaped, and finally left the unpleasantness) that the psychiatrist is (a) inattentive, (b) embittered, (c) stupid or (d) unfeeling, all of which are liabilities to the doctor-patient relationship.

"The second consideration that I promised sometime since is the matter of selective inattention as it pertains to the psychiatrist. In dealing with this I shall not repeat much that has been said before, but will quote the instance, which is by no means uncommon in working with patients, of the psychiatrist being charged with inattentions. Long experience with myself and others engaged in participant observation impresses me that whenever one is charged with having been particularly inattentive to something which the patient was trying to communicate, that the first hypothesis to be entertained—the hypothesis *always* to be entertained first—is that the patient is making a simple statement of fact—but nonetheless a statement which may well be subjected to validation as to its meaning.

"One of the most useful observations that anyone can make is that everything starts sometime, under some circumstances. It may well be taken to be a first principle in formulating all validating operations concerned with the patient's view of the psychiatrist, that one seeks to elicit [or discover] the beginning of the phenomenon. This does not mean that one asks fatuous questions like:

" 'When did I first ignore the matter that you are discussing?'

"An operation in point [with the purpose of discovering when or how something originated] might take the form of the psychiatrist pausing after listening to the statement of how inattentive he had been and saying:

" 'Let me see, do you recall what we were dealing with when you first tried to tell me this?'

"But the general aspect of the inquiry, the way it's said and so on, should be calculated to encourage recall—not to warn the patient that the clever psychiatrist is about to show him up, or, even more unfortunately, not to communicate the notion that the psychiatrist is now going to sneak or squirm out of an admission of his fault. This notion that everything starts sometime and under some circumstances can hardly be overemphasized as a principle to have in mind when one is exploring something pertaining to the patient's view of the psychiatrist whose performance has been this or that." [9]

A condensation of this description of the psychiatrist's therapeutically intended activity would suggest that by finding himself in a complicated interpersonal situation with the patient— that is, participating in mental illness—the psychiatrist can convert this very complexity into a subject of study by both participants, and by so doing, simplify the situation by reorienting the activity of both toward their mutual goal. In Sullivan's language this means to substitute mental health for mental illness.

If the first of Dr. Sullivan's descriptions identifies and describes as illness a process which would not ordinarily be thought of in these terms, his other specific "dynamisms of difficulty" sound more familiar as he starts to describe them because they are more generally recognized. He treated obsessional substitution quite fully, schizophrenic and paranoid processes, and hysterical phenomena, in the course of the lec-

[9] This quotation from Sullivan is taken from unpublished material. See copyright page.

tures. We cannot touch each of these here, but some discussion of the obsessional state may help to demonstrate in a different way the utility of his method of analysis in interpersonal terms.

Sullivan often began a discussion of a particular syndrome with a general remark about all mental illness. "Now the first risk that the psychiatrist has to contend with is that he is going to diagnose the patient. If out of what we have discussed you have a picture of *people* falling into clinical groups or categories . . . you have missed the whole point of the presentation. *Everything* that can be found in mental disorder can be found in anyone, but the accent, the prominence, the misuse of that which is found in the mental patient, is more or less characteristic. That does not in any sense mean that the mental patient lacks any of the common human heritage—and therefore when you start your contact with a patient, you must understand that you are in touch primarily with a human being remarkably like you, though significantly different. Now if on careful analysis of the significant difference you find an outstanding pattern of misfortune, then, if you wish, you may classify the patient on this outstanding pattern of misfortune. But that does not mean that he will not show everything else about the human personality in his personal relations that we have ever encountered." [10]

Obsessional substitution he identified in careful but relatively familiar terms [11]—"The group of processes that we wish to discuss show themselves as the monopolizing of the focus of attention by noted symbol processes which complicate the identifying of the satisfaction-seeking aspect of the situation. These noted, recognized symbol processes themselves carry an appreciation of, or a recognition of, their importance with respect to the avoiding of anxiety, or the protection of one's self-esteem . . .

[10] This quotation from Sullivan is taken from unpublished material. See copyright page.

[11] Sullivan specifies obsessional substitution as follows: (1) when a "ritual" or series of arguments or other performances whose purpose is not intended to be open to inference on the basis of observable behavior is provoked and (2) when or to the extent that the person manifesting the behavior does not have any clear awareness of what provoked it, we call such behavior obsessional substitution.—The Editor.

but however much they may be recognized as such, they include no recognition of, no hint of, the relation which anxiety *might* have if it occurred, to any specific satisfaction-seeking process which has called them out. In other words, they are variously representative of the self-system, they occupy [or tend to monopolize] awareness, and they give no hint at all of *what* has disturbed the self-system." He described many types of preoccupation in detail, systematically, and then what happens in the household when preoccupation is conspicuous; all descriptions and classifications were in terms of what happened with others, or better, in the integration with others. His illustrations include many which have not been considered as preoccupation by others—for instance, the patient who is "resisting the impulse" to do something or other—for Sullivan this contains no hint at all of the type of tension which calls out the preoccupation. Many types of preoccupation can be recognized as preoccupation only by their effect and the place of their appearance in an interpersonal situation. On one occasion certain concerns may include no element of protection of self-esteem, but identically expressed in other situations may be used repeatedly as stressful interferences in cooperative behavior serving clearly the avoidance of anxiety.

One illustration—a favorite one—can be given:

"Among these so-called morbid elements of stressful interference of cooperation, I'd like especially to call your attention to misunderstandings, especially of the sort which I call the 'fly-paper' kind. Now I don't know how many of you have seen, in nature or the comics, a cat getting away from a sheet of fly-paper in which it is stuck. But the peregrinations of the fly-paper and the cat are singularly suggestive of this type of misunderstanding. The other fellow is injured by something you say, and you are a little shocked, and so you correct him; but lo, what you have said in correcting him has wounded the person still more deeply and after a few [ex]changes of this sort, you'll find yourself so completely stuck up in misunderstandings that you and the cat simply have everything in common." [12]

[12] This quotation from Sullivan is taken from unpublished material. See copyright page.

He emphasized that he had observed patients who were heavily documented as obsessional develop schizophrenic disorders, and stated quite flatly that "I doubt if it is possible for humanity at this state of its existence to differentiate the two. All obsessional conditions have as a possibility the development of grave schizophrenic conditions . . . I hope by these remarks to suggest that, however grave a problem to the therapist an obsessional neurosis is, it is not the gravest thing that could happen to the patient—so that he has a little right to cling to what he has, before giving it up to see what might happen to him." [13]

How does the psychiatrist recognize obsessional substitution? Again Sullivan describes step by step how obsessional complication is suspected and then validated in the participant observation which is the psychiatric interview. In the course of the interview a remark is made which calls out the complication and which the psychiatrist notes. "This often takes the form of a moralistic so-called semi-irrelevancy, often a reply which indicates that the remark in question was regarded as disparaging the patient's worth. Now one very wisely defers forming any hypotheses when one experiences this sort of thing until one has done at least a little checking up with what happened . . .

"While one can easily cause anxiety in a person using nothing more complicated than selective inattention, there is very little danger of your causing severe anxiety in a person enjoying obsessional substitution; and so if the moralistic or disparaging misinterpretation does appear, it is quite safe to engage immediately in a supplementary operation to check what happened, and my experience has taught me that the type of operation which has great merit in such states is to say, 'I don't believe I understood,' or if you want to be still more abrupt, 'I don't follow.' Whereupon something else happens and if it is the same type or only more so, then one is perhaps justified in entertaining the hypothesis of obsessional substitution along with the following:

"First, that the cultural background of the patient is significantly different from that which the psychiatrist supposed it

[13] This quotation from Sullivan is taken from unpublished material. See copyright page.

was . . . Secondly, that the patient has been misled as to what the psychiatrist wants to hear. A large number of people try to guess what you want to hear, and if they guess badly then they sound very obsessional . . . and the third hypothesis: that the patient did not understand the comment (same old hypothesis as last time) yet for some reason did not seek to find out what was meant . . . The fourth hypothesis—that the patient did understand the comment, the meaning of which to him [the patient], the psychiatrist did not understand. It is perfectly remarkable how many times psychiatrists insult people with a most blissful ignorance of their insolence. Under those circumstances, of course, the [patient's] reactions are not proof of the presence of obsessional substitution. And certainly not before the fifth [alternative] is the hypothesis to be entertained [and tested], that one is confronted with a person having habitual recourse to obsessional substitution . . ." [14]

Having traced such processes in the interpersonal history with patients, Sullivan shows clearly the originality of his particular method of analysis by observing and identifying difficulty in purely interpersonal terms. "Insofar as it has been necessary for people to get better by a glimpse far backward into how they could have become sick, I have been immensely impressed by the fact that these people had parents whom neighbors probably called hypocrites . . . Now if you would think *not* of what a hypocrite might mean to you but what it probably meant to the people who used it, I think you will find that it meant that they are people who could stymie you by saying things you did not believe, and you did not believe they believed—a skillful use of words in a specious way . . . Hypocrisy is [presumed to be manifested] when one uses traditionally significant verbal statements to condemn or embarrass others, but is not at all embarrassed by one's reference to these verbal formulae in the freedom of one's own behavior . . . It does not mean you are a crook . . . Hypocrites are not conscious, deliberate hypocrites. If you were trying to be a conscious deliberate hypocrite, you would prob-

[14] This quotation from Sullivan is taken from unpublished material. See copyright page.

ably get the reputation of being an extremely astute politician—
you would get places, you see . . . A person called behind his
back a hypocrite is a person who is using sublimation to really
devastating ends upon the environment. He is not wittingly doing
it; he has *unwittingly* found the socially tolerable if not socially
highly approved way of satisfying very destructive impulses.

"What happens to the child [of 'hypocritical' parents]? Children are under the compulsion of catching on to be human beings at a rate which, if it were clearly perceived by their parents,
would make parents erect bronze statues of children on public
squares . . . In early life there is no possibility for anyone to
express one's final resentment with the vicissitudes of living with
immunity.[15] But if you know how to do the trick with words, like
perhaps papa or mama does, that would be [or provide] escape
[from trouble] [16] . . . Children who are going to be obsessional
are horribly intrigued by the . . . really universe-neutralizing
power of verbal symbols, as used by the blissfully unwitting
parent who *always* puts the mate to complete disadvantage by
reference to an irrelevant but potent rationalization.

"You will realize that if any symbol operation shows such
miraculous power of immunizing one from anxiety, it has to be of
tremendous interest to the child . . . Insofar as hypocrisy is a
pattern to which the child is exposed, that child will regard
verbal operations as endowed with transcendental power. You
must understand that transcendental power means a capacity to
produce effect which no exercise of reason would lead one to
expect a thing to do . . . Now these children have seen father
get away with something that would be transcendental if *they*
could get away with it—and they go about seeing how to manip-

[15] The phrase "with immunity" probably qualifies "to express one's final
resentment."—The Editor.

[16] The transcription seems faulty here. Sullivan's meaning appears to be
that the child has the impression that if he could only discover the right
string of words—the magic symbols—he would be able to avoid or escape
a lot of pain, frustration, and anxiety, and perhaps do so in a manner
analogous to that of father when the latter, for example, "looks askance at
a pretty lady" and tells his wife she has an evil mind, etc., if she notices
what he is up to and demurs, thus reducing her to impotence or tears.—The
Editor.

ulate this transcendental power. It must reside in language symbols—what he [that is, father] says is what stymies mother." [17]

The child fails in his attempt to understand this, but "one of the curiosities of the Western culture is that if you become preoccupied in an imaginary, that is, an impossible problem, people will gradually come to respect you for your diligence . . . Any . . . recondite task followed consistently, which means that it is important to you, is apt to lead people to think that it is important, the reason being that most people know that what they do is not very important. So anybody who does anything seriously makes other people wonder if they are not engaged in something important . . . That in a strange sense is what children who are born into these homes learn; that if you are dreadfully busy with horribly problematic aspects of life—it doesn't matter what—people get to be terribly concerned with the importance of what you are interested in . . . Consequently any frontal attack on the problem of why this is important, is probably the greatest menace that the victim has to contend with. And do they contend with it? Many do. They have recourse to the most perfect answer in the world. That answer is: 'I don't know.' . . . So when some intellectual comes along and says, 'But why do you have to tie your shoes twice?' they say, 'I don't know, but I feel terrible if I don't.' The poor intellectual has to creep away; he has a vague feeling that that makes very good sense so he does not know what to do next . . . It would be very embarrassing if he stuck around. That is the awful reason, coupled with the history I spoke of, of why we have obsessional neurotics." [18]

If this then is the activity of the self-system occurring when anxiety is evoked, and the interpersonal history of this self-system activity, a remaining question is: what evoked the anxiety? Sullivan found this to be malevolence—which he described as follows. "The experience of tenderness, initially indispensable to personal survival, implies the evolution of beneficent activities, in accord

[17] This quotation from Sullivan is taken from unpublished material. See copyright page.

[18] This quotation from Sullivan is taken from unpublished material. See copyright page.

with one's opportunities; these patterns of activity, and the tendency to manifest and develop them, must be universal unless they have been disintegrated in later stages of development."

However if "the need for tenderness . . . [becomes] associated in experience with pain or anxiety, [it] will become hedged about with precautions. The recurrent experience of rebuff of the need for tenderness will lead to disintegration of patterns of tender action, or of the 'expression' of the need for tenderness,—in turn with the evolution of patterns of mischievous, malicious activity in situations now characterized by the foresight of rebuff.[19] Like other instances of the disintegration of a motivational system, this 'conversion into the opposite' involves important processes in the self-system; it represents a development of what may well be called standard misinterpretations of interpersonal reality which will be apt to endure from thenceforth, and occur without focal awareness—so that the person manifesting this disjunctive attitude in interpersonal relations can scarcely be expected to be clear in recognizing the fact that there has been at a fairly definite time in his personal history, such a change from a beneficent to a malicious attitude." [20] Such a change he called a "malevolent transformation."

So that finally "obsessional substitution is a self-system activity concerned with masking the malevolence which characterizes an interpersonal situation. This is done by more or less formal or ritualized covert and overt supplementary processes." [21]

And now again to follow one step farther than is usual—"It requires continuous reminder for me to feel content that you are not losing track of the fact that we are discussing interpersonal relations, not people as such, as units, and so I want at this time to take a little time out to illustrate to you how easy it is to know

[19] Judging from other lectures, I do not think Sullivan means to imply that when tenderness becomes hedged about with precautions it must lead to *disintegration* of patterns of tender action as this paragraph might lead one to believe.—The Editor.

[20] This quotation from Sullivan is taken from unpublished material. See copyright page.

[21] This quotation from Sullivan is taken from unpublished material. See copyright page.

where malevolence is. I will talk about one of my ultimately happy obsessional patients from whom I learned a great deal. This was a lady who suffered very serious difficulties in living with her mother, not to mention some chronic complication of gastric ulcer, which will darn near kill you, and so on. She seemed an exceedingly intelligent and well-informed person, and knew that psychiatry ought to be good for something—but instead of [treatment for] the difficulties with mother, she obtained treatment for something else. She was treated for [the] difficulty in living with her husband and went on to better hands for the solution of the problem of mother. Now in the course of human events, and you must understand how tedious a great many of them were, it came to pass that what was destroying the lady's viscera was an entirely unrecognized resentment provoked by a certain, very frequent repetition of a behavior pattern with her husband.[22] The lady who, in retrospect, was clearly entitled to be treated tenderly by a man—in retrospect because you see, I never think of persons as people while dealing with them—this lady frequently, O very frequently, sought to be treated tenderly by her husband, and was invariably rebuffed, and never noticed it, but her belly was in pretty bad shape. That was the general pattern of a great deal of my learning about obsessional substitution.

"But who the hell was malevolent to whom? Since she was, of course, my patient, after the best traditions of psychiatry, she was an extremely downtrodden and abused woman. That was quite self-evident, you see. But how about her husband? What about a bird who can't give tenderness at least once a day, probably usually two or three times a day put on the spot by demand for it? So you figure out where the malevolence was.

"Now the answer is, the malevolence was in the interpersonal relation. It does not make any sense to try to distribute these things . . . A discussion of a situation can clearly indicate malevolence, but when you get to deciding which is the more malevolent of the people in the situation, you are engaged in a

22 Note the unusual wording—not "provoked by her own actions" or "provoked by her husband." A. H. Stanton.

moral task, or something that is really rather beside the point in the study of interpersonal relations." [23]

Our following of Sullivan's description and analysis of two "mental disorders"—one familiar and one new—has illustrated his conception of psychiatry as the study of interpersonal relations, and the study of interpersonal relations only. But aside from such detailed treatments of special clinical problems, Sullivan of course offered the clinician much more which we can only mention. A central contribution was his form of thought; the student of Sullivan is prone not to fractionate his patient into different parts or to think of him in static terms. It is easy to think of the configuration of which the patient is a part without dividing his body and his mind, his mind and his environment, his intellect and his emotions, or to impose other arbitrary divisions upon him.

It is clear that if mental disorder is thought of as complicated interpersonal relations, the psychiatrist's position is a central one for social study. This can start at home. It is easy to understand that, as a corollary to this position, Sullivan would write articles with such unusual titles as "Notes on Investigation, Therapy and Education in Psychiatry and Their Relation to Schizophrenia." [24] These topics would have been treated as a unit by few others. The study of the social process in the mental hospital is but a slight extension of his line of inquiry. And it is our impression that his formulations are considerably in advance of those who attribute phenomena to either an abstract "culture" or, among psychiatrists, to the "group."

Sullivan's emphasis upon communication in the development of interpersonal relations, and in therapy, invites integration with current interest in information theory, and his views of anxiety constitute a criticism of many current analyses of communication. His formulations meet many of the recent criticisms of psychology made by Dewey and Bentley in their "Transactional" anal-

[23] This quotation from Sullivan is taken from unpublished material. See copyright page.

[24] This paper was published in *Psychiatry* in 1947 (10:271-280) and republished in *A Study of Interpersonal Relations.*—The Editor.

ysis.[25] And Sullivan's relation to general psychiatric practice may be summarized by the statement that when he insisted that psychiatry was the study of interpersonal relations, he made explicit something that every psychiatrist, of whatever type of practice, knows in his heart.

But the relationship of his ideas to those of psychoanalysis has been a recurrent difficulty to his students, his opponents, and to a less extent, to himself. He repeatedly cautioned against attempting to fuse—or confuse—the two methods of approach. The great and important reason for such caution is the fact that he dealt with a different subject matter. Psychoanalysis is a theory of the individual, of psychobiological structure and dynamics—Sullivan is a student of interpersonal relations, and his theoretical developments are strong precisely because of his restricting his subject matter to interpersonal relations. Occasionally conflicts and concurrences may be sought out from comparing the two, but usually such attempts are as confusing as those which would occur between one person playing checkers and another chess on the same board.

As Sullivan is followed carefully and seriously, a contribution in a different area becomes abundantly clear—he has made us aware of our ignorance. His theoretical framework throws it into sharp relief; it is no longer as easy for our ignorance to masquerade as knowledge behind plausible rationalizations and impressive verbalisms. And at the same time, it is a valuable tool for use in studying interpersonal relations. There is much that is inviting to explore.

[25] The reference is to Dewey and Bentley's Book, *Knowing and the Known.*—The Editor.

DISCUSSION

HERBERT STAVEREN
Washington School of Psychiatry

THERE seems to be no need to comment on the excellence of the two preceding papers or on the fact that the task of undertaking a summary of Sullivan's conceptions of psychiatry is indeed a gigantic one. It rather seems to me that one might profitably construct two of these hypothetical entities referred to as persons, and to select for purposes of illustration two such constructs from the rather extreme opposite ends of the spectrum, namely, one person who grew up in a home in which things went almost ideally well, and who might be called Joe Jones, and a second person whose home experience was more or less disastrous, and who might be called Sam Shaw. I propose to follow sketchily these two hypothetical people from birth into their middle teens.

Let us take our first look at the infants about two weeks after birth. Mrs. Jones, a rather comfortable and mature person who has long since learned to carefully think things through for herself and who has come to recognize that she seems to have rather sound judgment in a fairly high percentage of instances, has attended some meetings on child care during her pregnancy, she has familiarized herself with the biologic processes of pregnancy and birth, and she has not found it too difficult to seek expert information whenever and wherever indicated. Her relationship with her husband is satisfactory and relatively unencumbered by in-law complications. Labor and the production of a healthy infant have left her with a certain sense of achievement, without undue pride, however, but rather with the realization that she is doing a biologic and interpersonal job that has been done many times before, with varying degrees of success.

The period following her return from the hospital is rather smooth; there is neither need to be martyred in motherhood nor need to brag about her unique accomplishment. She is apt to enjoy her return to her husband and home, and she is likely to be keenly interested in, that is, astutely observant of, what might be going on between her and her newborn infant. Feeding schedules to her will be a rough guide line, not a threat, and most of the time she will rely on her power to recognize needs, and move appropriately to satisfy them. She herself will, perhaps without clear awareness, have a need to tend to her child's needs, that is to manifest tenderness, and thus powerfully motivated towards conjunctive integration with the child, her ministrations will be attended by a sense of well-being rather than to be perceived as chores. Under such circumstances the child is apt to lead an existence relatively free from anxiety. As tissue tensions, and perhaps also the tensions growing from the need for physical contact, arise, they will be relieved by well-timed and appropriate responses on the part of the observant mother, and since the mother in turn experiences well-being, that is, freedom from anxiety, in thus functioning tenderly, the child's empathic experience of the mother's emotional state will add to his state of relative euphoria. This being the preponderant experience, the child is apt not to become too gun-shy when occasional delays in having his tissue tensions relieved or flurries of empathic disturbance give him his first acquaintance with the highly unpleasant experience of anxiety.

The situation is quite different in the Shaw household. Mrs. Shaw, whose pregnancy was fairly stormy because she "did not really know whether she wanted this child and felt she ought to feel guilty about even thinking such things, for after all her poor husband couldn't help being what he was, what with a mother like his, who was so much worse than her own, who was really a darling, only there had been something, maybe too much love and devotion, and she had felt for a while that she had married her husband more to get away from her mother than because she loved him, but of course she had never told him any of this. It is so hard to tell people things, or ask them things, like that doctor, for instance, what was his name now, funny she could think only of obstetrician, but that was what he did and not his name, and, oh yes, there were things she felt she ought to know, she supposed they were anatomical things, but then she had never been good at such things, and about sterilizing things, weren't babies supposed to be more or less sterilized . . ." And she went into labor frightened and uninformed. And she told her husband, both mothers and her doctor that everything was fine, just as it should be, only would she be able to handle the situation? And she left the hospital just as frightened and uninformed, with two additional burdens, one the actual child who to her was a fearsome thing all tangled up with chores, alarm clocks, failures and what not, and the other a terrible secret: when she awoke from the anesthetic and was shown her child, she had expected to be flooded by mother love. That was when it was supposed to happen, wasn't it? Well, it didn't.

On coming home, she wasn't sure whether she felt well or not, whether she should do things or rest, and mainly she worried about not knowing what to do if the baby should start crying. She had already observed that all crying sounded the same, so how was she to know whether he was hungry, wet or what. And within a few days she knew that she did not know, because it seemed that whatever she did, he not only did not stop crying, but seemed to cry more loudly. Thank God for the feeding schedule, that at least would tell her when he was hungry, even though it was such a nuisance, particularly since she never knew whether the bottles were really sterile. And then there was this other matter, the diapers. Well, no use even thinking about *that*. Under these circumstances Sam is apt to have a hectic time. Since anxiety and uncertainty constantly interfere with his mother's powers of observation, and even more with her need or wish to manifest tenderness, that is, tend to his needs, the tensions aroused by tissue needs are apt to go unrelieved for long periods of time, which in itself probably subjects him to bouts of prolonged anxiety. But worse, and more continuously, most contact with his mother is apt to be poisoned by empathically experienced anxiety. But since there are few unmitigatedly evil situations, this one is apt to change for the better in some ways.

Mrs. Shaw, utterly exhausted from two weeks of "caring for that child," finally surrenders and accepts her mother's—or her mother-in-law's—generous offer to come and stay with her for a month or two or three. And while Mrs. Shaw's life is made more unbearable by the presence of a matriarch, who thrives on pointing out to the new mother that "when I raised my five children, I did this, that and the other thing much better . . ." And while this new ordeal causes a great increase in Mrs. Shaw's distress and in her son's empathically experienced anxiety while in contact with his mother, there now are fewer contacts between mother and son, and much of the immediate care of the infant is carried by grandmother. Now while grandmother has, some twenty-odd years ago, poisoned her daughter's childhood, she has long since settled into a reasonably comfortable state of obsessional righteousness, and no uncertainties beset her at the prospect of caring for her grandson. And as she takes over, with perhaps a trace of well-being even, because for once she is right and more competent, little Sam gets his needs attended to a little faster and more appropriately, and as the anxiety from that source diminishes, there is less crying, and in turn his mother is made less anxious by not knowing what he is crying for or about, so that there is even a lessening of empathic distress, and as a result there is even a possibility, or even a likelihood, that Mrs. Shaw will have moments of being able to manifest tenderness and enjoy it, and notice that her son is responding by manifesting a sense of well-being. And as Mrs. Shaw shifts from the highly unpleasant contacts with her mother, contacts which are full of "You see, I told you so," and moves more toward living with her son, the situation improves sufficiently to warrant suggesting that grandmother now leave. And after a day or two of grandmother-less bliss, the pattern of uncertainty in mother leading to poor observation of son, leading to poor response to his needs, leading to anxiety in son, leading to anxiety in mother, leading to empathically transmitted anxiety in son, etc., is resumed. Only this time Mrs. Shaw swears that she will not ask her mother to return, this time she will use the pediatrician.

But, being concerned about what people think about her, she does not dare call him for several days, and when she finally does call him, it is during the two A.M. feeding period, when Sam is particularly cranky, her husband angrily pretending sleep, and she herself is at her wits' end. And the pediatrician, called out of bed by an uncommunicative message about a child's crying, inquires about how much formula has been taken, how many stools, etc., and discovers nothing warranting a night call, and so expresses his displeasure with one of these neurotic mothers by appropriate brusqueness. It is apparent that the vicissitudes of Mrs. Shaw's subtle though serious mental disorder in a rather short time have filled with anxiety and rendered disjunctive not only her relationship with her newborn child, but probably for really useful purposes seriously damaged her relationship with her pediatrician, and of course further aggravated her probably already bad relationship with her husband, mother, etc.

Let us now take a look at the same children at the age of two. Joe Jones probably has exceeded standard expectations. He is likely to be well coordinated in his movements, he will have a good weight distribution and will be generally well proportioned. He will walk and talk like the human being that he is. There is apt to be between his mother and him a pattern of interaction which is predominantly satisfying to both. There will be a rather high degree of good verbal and non-verbal communication, and through the channels of empathy there is apt to flow the entire rainbow of shadings of emotional experience, without any undue emphasis on any particular one. On the whole, while anxiety will have been experienced many times, and on some occasions quite painfully, the total balance of well-being and anxiety is apt to be in favor of the former. The child will be an integrated member of the household, neither tyrant nor nuisance, and the satisfactions derived by the parents from the relationship with him are apt to be such as to predispose them towards having another child about this time.

Not so in the Shaw household. Long periods of crying are apt to be the rule, and irritability probably runs high among the parents. There will have been by that time many scenes in which Sam is blamed for this, that or the other as if he were a hardened, adult criminal. He is apt to be not as well proportioned as Joe Jones, and along with fluctuations in the general anxiety level in the family, there probably were alternating periods of anorexia and overeating, many illnesses mostly of tensional origin, with resulting abnormalities of weight. Muscular coordination is likely to be poor, and as a result sitting, walking, talking will not have appeared smoothly, but either early, associated with some distortion or incompleteness, or quite a bit later than usual. And since any deviation from what is supposed to be standard is apt to arouse anxiety in Mrs. Shaw because of what certain people might think of her for having an "abnormal" child, etc., the maturation of the various processes, already interfered with and distorted by excessive anxiety, will suffer further damage from anxiety evoked by the fact that the child at this early age presents unmistakable evidence that things have gone wrong. Probably long before this, Mrs. Shaw will have recognized that certain difficulties in her son seem to have been aggravated by her own anxieties, and she will resent him, and has resented him all along, for, in a way, having become a living witness to, and evidence of, her own difficulties in living. And she is going to be made anxious by such recognition and will have tried, and will go on trying to hide the outward manifestations of her resentment, by becoming restrictive, overprotective, overdemonstrative—in other words, "devoted."

But Sam, probably largely by way of the empathic linkage, will not only perceive the disturbance in his mother, but will be unable to respond to her "devotion" in any way acceptable to her. In such a situation, by the time the child is two years old, such masses of anxiety have been generated on all sides, that the relationship between mother and child is undoubtedly malevolently integrated. While in the Jones family most situations are likely to be integrated in some sort of conjunctive fashion,

with all members of the family in general moving towards satisfaction of needs, their own as well as those of the rest of the
household, a sufficient number of substitutive processes will have
been set in motion in the Shaw family so that it is highly probable that simple situations will seldom occur, satisfactions of
needs will be few or incomplete, and the predominant patterns
of integration will be disjunctive. And while Joe is likely to have
a large "Good Me," a small "Bad Me" and either a microscopic
or non-existent "Not Me," the state of affairs is apt to be almost
reversed in the Shaw family, with "Bad Me" towering high above
"Good Me," and much experience having already been relegated
to "Not Me."

   I have so far given you a bird's-eye view of our hypothetical
people in infancy and childhood, and now want to examine what
has happened to them after a couple of years in the juvenile era,
let us say at the beginning of the third grade. Beginning with
Joe Jones, we probably would find him having successfully navi-
gated some of the reefs of the juvenile era, that is, not having
undergone a malevolent transformation, he is capable of integrating situations with adults and compeers with the expectation of
a certain degree of satisfaction, and in turn will be able to observe a good many factors involved in each situation, and to
respond adequately to them, which further results in a relatively
high percentage of adequate responses from others, and with
this a reasonable amount of satisfactions and a sense of his own
competence. The conjunctive patterns of integration prevailing,
he has the maximum freedom to learn what each period of maturation, each phase of new experience, has to offer. So, in the
third grade, he will have learned a good deal about healthy competition, about winning in some instances and losing in others,
without either being of earth-shaking import. He will have
learned some of the advantages of cooperation, and, most important, he will have been adequate and free enough to have
undergone with profit the initially always painful indoctrination
into the need for healthy compromise. Because "Bad Me" is relatively small, the reduction of his parents from the god-like figures of his early universe to simple human beings with some

special significance to him is apt to be taken in stride, and as a result, his relationships within the home not only do not interfere with, but actually can further, his need to integrate situations with other exponents of the social order, such as classmates, children in the block, teachers, cops, other strangers. There are apt to be interests in activities appropriate to his age, skills and experience, that is, there is likely to be an exercise of talents and powers as they mature and become discovered. A fairly high percentage of his important communications with others probably occurs in the syntaxic mode, and it is highly probable that he is fairly articulate in identifying, and therefore rather well acquainted with, his various needs, and with some of the ways and means open to him in finding satisfaction for these needs.

Looking at Sam Shaw, however, we are apt to see a disastrously different picture. Although only in the third grade, he is already attending his fifth school, numerous problems in relating himself to others as well as in the quality of his school work, plus inextricable difficulties occurring in all parent-teacher contacts, have led repeatedly to either the mother's withdrawing him from school, more or less in outraged dignity, or else to the school's suggesting that maybe Sam would be happier in some other school. On closer view all of Sam's attempts at integrating situations seem to be characterized by malevolence, that is, there will be mischief and malice in his approach to people, or subtler forms thereof, such as the expectation of an unfavorable response regardless of what he may do himself. And as others find their interest in relating themselves to this odd child waning after a number of unsuccessful attempts—in other words, as eventually the responses called out by Sam's malevolent patterns actually undergo a malevolent transformation—his expectations become confirmed and further precipitate him on the path toward greater and greater malevolence. Friendships, of course, cannot be formed under such circumstances, neither can there be sufficient conjunctive relatedness to a group, and as a result of this lack of a medium in which learning can occur, the interpersonal processes characteristic of the juvenile period, such as healthy competition, cooperation and compromise, are not acquired. Usually the family is of little use in this situation: in the first place the parents tend to be handicapped by their own anxieties and malevolent patterns; and in the second place, what capacities for positive integration there exist, let us say, in Mrs. Shaw are more or less put out of commission by her anxiety aroused by beholding the growing warp in her son, a warp which she knows, certainly for brief periods of time, to be the outcome of the disastrous interaction between herself and her son.

In taking these two boys into preadolescence one can see the divergence of their paths becomes even more spectacular. All along Joe Jones' progress has been like the fitting into place of the pieces of a picture puzzle; as new capacities mature, as new patterns of integration become evolved, relationships and the social structure of Joe's environment seem to be prepared for the exercise of such capacities. Preexisting patterns of integration seem to have paved the way for new skills and abilities to be learned and put to use. So we find Joe in his early teens not only an active participant in various groups and group functions, but already well established in one or more intimate chum relationships. He comes to this stage of development with a great deal of experience, much of which has been well formulated. And so he is ready for this almost most exciting and expansive step in maturation where someone like himself, chosen by himself, and esteemed the way he esteems himself enters with him into a relationship of equality, an equality which permits of the greatest amount of unreserved sharing of all kinds of experience, of new evaluations, explorations. There occurs in such a relationship the gradual progression from the more juvenile pattern of cooperating to the more enduring one of collaborating, which is essential for the patterning of later adult relationships.

In the case of Sam it is exactly this very important period of development which, because of the almost inevitable disasters it will bring, is such a crucial period of his life that one might say that even a modicum of success might save him from the most serious outcome of his mental disorder. The accumulation of failures and humiliations of the juvenile period, his by now probably extreme isolation, which is not lessened by even frantic attempts to copy patterns of relatedness he can see his compeers have, his extreme deficiency in syntaxic communication, the improbability of his having learned even the superficial rudiments of patterns which facilitate one's getting along in groups, the much too frequent experience of having his malevolent outlook confirmed, and thereby justified, all these events of his life up to preadolescence leave him almost totally unprepared for the experience of intimacy.

He will watch his compeers gradually pair off, and with envy he will notice the development of experiences between them which he knows he needs. He will however not be able to identify the various factors that have gone into leaving him so poorly equipped for a relationship of intimacy. He will long for it, the way any lonely person would, but without being in a position to make any active moves toward another individual. Should it be his good fortune that another boy would move toward him, it is highly probably that within a short time such large discrepancies in functioning capacities will become evident, that either the relationship will develop into one of a stronger person leading a cripple, or else the other boy will not find it compatible with maintaining his own integrity to continue an inevitably one-sided relationship. In either instance, it probably remains a toss-up whether the benefits gained from even this short attempt at intimacy will outweigh the painful experience of losing what had been so briefly and precariously attained. On the whole, with a life course such as we have postulated for Sam, it is much more likely that there will be neither attempt at, nor opportunity for, forming even a pseudo-chum relationship. Partly this will be on the basis of discrepancy in age, that is, Sam is apt to reach comparative readiness for even an attempt at preadolescent behavior much later than his chronological compeers, so that he will be faced with well-patterned relationships all around him, while he is still alone. Partly it will be because there probably are few personalities which on a preadolescent level will undertake a relationship with a thoroughly malevolent chum.

I hope that these two hypothetical boys have illustrated to some extent the living application of some of Sullivan's conceptions. I am interrupting the stories at the preadolescent level, because it is probable that the bulk of the important patterns of relating oneself to others have been evolved and pretty much fixed at this time, and what follows is merely a more or less logical extrapolation of the curve of development from birth to preadolescence.

SULLIVAN AS A CLINICIAN

CHAPTER III

SULLIVAN AND PSYCHOANALYSIS

CLARA THOMPSON

William Alanson White Institute

SULLIVAN credited three great therapists with significantly influencing his thinking in psychiatry, Sigmund Freud, Adolf Meyer, and William A. White. From each, he acquired certain aspects of his approach to the problems of mental illness. From Freud, he obtained many fundamental orientations. Through Meyer, he was influenced in his thinking of mental illness as a dynamic pattern of behavior, as a way of reacting to life, and from White, he acquired some of the practical aspects of his therapeutic approach. Meyer and White directly influenced his life through personal contact and teaching. Sullivan never met Freud but he was an earnest student of his writings.

He entered the field of psychiatry around 1920. Unlike Freud, his first contacts were with psychotic patients. He only later became interested in the problems of the neurotic and in character disorders. For many years, he devoted his research to an attempt to apply psychoanalytic theory and technique to the therapy of the psychotic. Jung and Bleuler before him had found psychoanalytic theory useful in explaining some of the behavior and symbolization of the psychotic, but psychoanalysis as a method of therapy for the psychotic had hardly begun. In fact, it was considered dangerous and is still so considered to treat the psychotic by the classical Freudian methods. It was believed that classical analysis could precipitate psychosis in a borderline case and that therefore all attempts at psychoanalyzing psychotics should be avoided. At the same time, much of Freud's thinking was creeping into the orientation of psychiatrists in America. The importance of the experiences of early childhood in producing later difficulties was being stressed. Freud's concept of the unconscious, resistance, repression, and transference were beginning to be considered in observing patients. Meyer did not subscribe to Freud's idea of transference as a sexual attachment to the analyst. In fact, he hoped the whole problem could be avoided by a frequent change of therapist, thus discouraging too great attachment to any one person. White was much more accepting of Freud's thinking than Meyer and encouraged those working under him to experiment with Freud's methods. Some others who had had direct contact with Freud, the most outstanding of whom was Brill, were using Freudian psychoanalytic methods without modification in their therapy with neurotics. This briefly was the attitude towards psychoanalysis in America around 1920.

The American Psychoanalytic Association had been formed. Its membership at that time did not consist exclusively of psychoanalysts, but included psychiatrists and neurologists interested in discussing and examining Freud's theories. Thus both Meyer and White were charter members, although neither would have considered himself a psychoanalyst. Although most psychiatrists were still resistant to Freud's theories, certain aspects of it were infiltrating psychiatric thinking, and there was a readiness on the part of a few to experiment with his methods, but even with these, the general attitude was inquiring and somewhat skeptical. Soon after 1920, an increasing number of psychiatrists began going to Europe to study psychoanalysis at first hand from Freud and his pupils, and by the late 1920s, psychoanalytic institutes had been formed in London, Berlin, Vienna, and Budapest, and many American psychiatrists were trained in these.

In the meantime, psychoanalysis in Europe, although not yet well known by the general public, had been applied in practice for twenty or twenty-five years by an ever increasing group of pupils around Freud. Freud in his own thinking had progressed a long way from his earliest observations. By 1920 he was on the verge of several important new formulations which were to alter some of the basic thinking in psychoanalysis and a few psychoanalysts, especially Rank, Ferenczi and Reich, were beginning to experiment with improving psychoanalytic technique. The time seemed ripe for new advances.

Two very important alterations in theory at this time were the formulation of the repetition compulsion, and the discovery that repressed aggression played fully as significant a part in producing neurosis as repressed sexuality. Thus it was seen that man was not completely dominated by the pleasure principle as Freud had originally thought, but there was an even more primitive and more insistent drive to repeat over and over earlier life experiences both pleasurable and unpleasurable. Freud thought that transference was an example of this. One repeated with the analyst one's early relationships, be they erotic, hostile or whatever. The discovery of the importance of aggression led Freud to modify his instinct theory, but a discussion of this is not particularly pertinent here. Two other formulations at this time also influenced later thinking. One was Freud's new formulation of anxiety as the basis of the development of neurosis. It was seen clearly for the first time that symptoms and other defensive activities were developed to cope with and prevent awareness of anxiety. It was also at this time that Freud first formulated his theory of the total personality with his hypothetical invention of the concepts of ego, superego and id. This offered a theoretical basis for the study of character structure. Thus four important new ideas were presented which greatly influenced later alterations in therapy and theory. These were the repetition compulsion, the discovery of the importance of aggression, and the new formulation of the role of anxiety and the concept of the way the total personality functioned.

Other factors were also at work to produce change. There was an increasing dissatisfaction with therapeutic results. It seemed that analysis had become too theoretical. Patients dutifully recalled their childhood experiences but they did not improve. This stimulated Ferenczi and Rank to experimentation with technique, and both concluded, although in somewhat different terms, that a vital emotional relationship to the analyst was essential to cure. It was thought that analysts had gone too far in eliminating their personalities from the picture, that in carrying out the idea of being a mirror reflecting back to the patient only his own thoughts, they had created a situation in which no true emotion could be experienced. Both felt that it should be recognized that the analyst's personality must figure in the situation. Both advocated a less authoritarian attitude even to the point of admission of limitations and mistakes. Wilhelm Reich, utilizing the concept of character structure as a defensive system, a kind of protective armor, instituted another form of activity. He thought one must first show the patient that he defends himself against something, next point out to him the way in which he does it, and only then is he in a position to learn what is the danger from which he is protecting himself. The effect of these innovations was to make the reactions in the analytic situation much more important than the recall of the past, although the latter was not eliminated. This inevitably focused attention on the doctor-patient relationship.

Thus beginning about 1925 and continuing to the present time, analysis has concerned itself more and more with what is going on between people. The new therapeutic approach was called resistance analysis in contrast to the earlier method of seeking to uncover the childhood amnesia by free association. It was discovered that by the analyst's concentrating his interpretations almost entirely on the resistances, all other aspects of analysis took care of themselves. Furthermore, it was and is conceded that a character defense almost never disappears by simple free association. Some form of pointing out to the patient how he is defending himself is necessary in order to direct his attention in the proper channels.

This was the psychiatric world into which Sullivan entered in 1920. Working under William A. White at St. Elizabeth's Hospital, he was given every encouragement to explore that world. Since the material with which he must work was for the most part psychotic patients and predominantly schizophrenics, he first turned his energy to applying Freud's thinking to the understanding of schizophrenia, and his earliest papers show a close adherence to Freud's thinking.

It is interesting that although he was not directly in contact with psychoanalysis in Europe, some of his early innovations closely paralleled those developing in Europe. When Ferenczi was in the United States in 1926, Sullivan met him and found his thinking the most congenial to his own way of thinking of any of the analysts. At the same time, it would be an exaggeration to say that they influenced each other to any extent. Their contact was too brief, and each continued to develop without further communication with each other.

As you know, Freud was of the opinion that the narcissistic neuroses, by which he meant psychosis, could not be reached therapeutically by psychoanalysis. He believed these people to be incapable of an object attachment; therefore, they could not form a transference to the therapist, and no significant communication could take place. Sullivan was not convinced of this, although it was obvious that a mute catatonic patient was not communicating by free association. Nevertheless, Sullivan persisted in the idea that the patient was saying something by his behavior, and it was a question of finding a method of rapprochement. Thus came about his first innovations in technique.

Since the psychotic patient would not lie on a couch and would not free associate, Sullivan attempted to make contact with the patient in whatever situation was possible. With a mute catatonic, he often carried on soliloquies by the patient's bedside for many months. In them he would discuss the kinds of problems that bothered people, watching closely for any signs of response. He also discovered that some patients who were afraid of their hostility were more comfortable if a third person was in the room or near by and so on. Out of this early work, Sullivan became convinced that the psychotic was capable of transference in Freud's newer interpretation of it, in terms of the repetition compulsion, i.e., in his relation to the analyst, he was repeating earlier patterns of behavior. The difference, as Sullivan saw it, between a psychotic and neurotic transference was that in the psychotic almost all of the behavior was transference, and there was very little sense of current reality. Thus the analyst or employer was, in a manner of speaking, literally the father, and there was often no feeling of "*as if* you were my father." The problem then was to find some means of making the patient aware of the physician in his own right, which was quite a departure from the idea of the physician as a mirror. So at almost the same time that Ferenczi and Rank were discussing the importance of considering the physician's real personality as a factor in cure, Sullivan had come to a similar conclusion by a different route.

By 1929, Sullivan was beginning to formulate his approach in terms of what was later to become his theory of interpersonal relations. At about this time, he came in contact with the growing interest on the part of anthropologists in the study of comparative cultures. He was especially influenced in this field by Edward Sapir and Ruth Benedict. He saw in the study of comparative cultures an opportunity to test the universal validity of some of Freud's basic assumptions.

By the middle 1930s, Sullivan had begun to consolidate his own thinking as a result of these various influences and his own work with patients. I think I have shown convincingly that his own development stemmed directly from a psychoanalytic orientation and that in many ways he was a product of the current thinking of that time.

Sullivan's therapeutic technique which will be described by Dr. Mary White, although containing many details which are definitely his contribution and the result of his experience, has in its general theory much in common with the more active character analysis technique described by Wilhelm Reich and practiced pretty generally by analysts today. Since Reich's book was not translated into English until around 1940, and since Sullivan did not read German with ease, we have again the experience of his having discovered simultaneously, and as a result of his own experience many things which do not deviate greatly from the discoveries of others. In other words, the need to make the patient aware of his characteristic defensive maneuvers with people had been increasingly forcing itself upon therapists. The fact that independent attempts to solve this problem had much in common would seem to confirm the validity of the methods used.

To borrow an expression of Sullivan's, consensual validation is one of the ways of checking reality.

However, Sullivan went beyond Reich in certain respects, possibly because in dealing with the psychotic, he had a different problem. Reich felt that his method could not be used with anxious patients or borderline psychotics. It is precisely in this area that Sullivan perfected his technique. I think the unique contribution which he made was the ever present awareness of the need to convey respect for the patient and to maintain the patient's own self-esteem. Sullivan was perhaps too concerned with the fragility of patients because his first work was with psychotics, but this concern kept his approach always attuned to what the patient can stand. He was well aware of indications of approaching panic. On the other hand, he knew that premature interpretations could also make the patient more defensive. Thus he did not have to warn students not to use his method with anxious patients but rather to be very careful to use it correctly and with sensitivity.

There are two current misconceptions about the relation of Sullivan's methods and ideas to psychoanalysis. One group claims that what Sullivan taught is not psychoanalysis; the other group, in complete contradiction, insists that Sullivan says the same things as Freud but in different words. To clarify the first assumption requires a definition of psychoanalysis. If the term is to be used only for therapy, which subscribes without question to all of Freud's hypotheses, then it is true that what Sullivan taught is not psychoanalysis. If by psychoanalysis one means recognition of unconscious motivation, the influence of repression and resistance on the personality and the existence of transference, then Sullivan's thinking fulfills all requirements for being considered psychoanalysis. He himself was not concerned with this point and preferred to call his therapeutic approach intensive psychotherapy. I have already indicated the points at which his technique parallels current psychoanalytic method, and I can only say if Sullivan's methods are not psychoanalytic, then all character analysis methods are not psychoanalytic.

When we come to Sullivan's theory of personality, however, we find a definite deviation from Freud's thinking. Since both

Sullivan and Freud were observing human behavior, it is inevitable that some of their observations are very similar. The basic
difference is in a different philosophy of personality development. Freud's attention was called first to the unfortunate effects
of sexual repression in a society and at a time when this was an
ever present problem, i.e., in the late nineteenth century in
Vienna. This weighted his thinking in terms of the struggle of
man to keep his instincts sufficiently under control to conform to
the society in which he lived. Freud did not alter this basic
orientation when he later enlarged his instinct theory to include
aggression. If you will, Sullivan also starts with the assumption
of a basic drive in man—one towards growth and maturation. He
rather unfortunately, I think, uses the word power for this drive.
Sexual maturation would be but one aspect of this drive. Having
postulated this basic need for growth, his interest then shifts to
a study of the acculturation process. The need to grow means
the need to master one's environment, and that means learning
the pattern of the culture, its speech, its customs, its taboos. Thus
the human organism with his potential drive for development
becomes in time patterned to the society in which he lives. So
while Freud sees the child's development as going on inevitably
in terms of the child's sexual development and his libido, Sullivan's child is a product of his interaction with significant people.
He assumes that the need for security is even stronger in the
human being than the need for instinctual gratification or satisfaction and that these latter become problems only when they
conflict with the need for security. Since man is the least instinct-
dominated of all the animals, it behooves us according to Sullivan to concern ourselves chiefly with the forces which do dom-
inate man, and they are the social forces.

He divides the human being's development into six periods—
first, infancy, the period from birth to the acquisition of language.
This roughly corresponds in time to Freud's oral stage, but what
Sullivan stresses at this time is the learning process, the gradual
development of awareness in the infant of himself as a separate
entity. A kind of communication exists already in the form of
empathy with the mother. The second stage, childhood, extends
from the beginning of the learning of language to the time when

interest in playing with other children develops. In this period, many of the basic requirements of the culture, such as toilet training, are taught, and the child is chiefly associated with adults. Interest in feces and genitals are a part of the child's learning process, and at this time he becomes more aware of and more active in his relationship to his parents. The third stage, the juvenile era, begins with developing interest in one's compeers. The child learns to cooperate and compete. In these three stages, Sullivan considers that sex as it is known to the adult does not figure.

With preadolescence, the capacity to care for the happiness of someone else as much as for one's own appears for the first time, and Sullivan considers this the most important period in terms of acculturation. If the child does not succeed at this period in forming a close bond with a contemporary, he will go through life isolated and gravely handicapped. The chum is not necessarily a sexual partner at this stage, although he may become so later. With the beginning of adolescence, sex for the first time becomes an important factor in the personality development. Here characteristically Sullivan does not see sex *per se* as a problem, but rather the cultural attitudes about it constitutes the hazard. Since we frown upon extra-marital sexual activity and postpone marriage, the adolescent has great difficulty in gaining satisfaction and at the same time security. The sixth stage extends from late adolescence to maturity. Maturity is achieved when one has successfully formed a relationship of durable intimacy with another person. Thus Sullivan's system of personality development is constructed around the concept of acculturation; it is the result of interpersonal processes, while Freud's system is predominantly related to the sexual impulse, the libido and sublimations of it. Sullivan believed the sexual impulse was not sufficiently important prior to puberty to have a decisive influence on personality development.

One can, of course, find some rough correlations between Freud's system and Sullivan's. At least some of the transition points correspond in time. Thus the transition from oral to anal phase occurs at approximately the time when Sullivan notes the transition from infancy to childhood. The latency period of

Freud also roughly corresponds in time to Sullivan's juvenile era, but the frame of orientation is entirely different, and the aspects in the child's behavior in those periods stressed by the two men are quite different. Moreover, there is nothing in Freud's system which at all corresponds to Sullivan's conception of preadolescence. Sullivan's observations of this period are a unique contribution. Nevertheless, there is no doubt that Sullivan's thinking was greatly influenced by Freud. He undoubtedly gave Freud's theory earnest consideration as he was formulating his own, and some of the observations which Freud made but did not specifically include in his theory are important parts of Sullivan's theory, e.g., the significance of the child's attitude towards the parents during the period of toilet training was mentioned by Freud but is stressed by Sullivan; Sullivan also adds to this the recognition of the importance of the parents' attitude in this activity as well.

When one comes to a consideration of Sullivan's concept of parataxic distortion, the self-system and anxiety, many claim that these are simply different names for Freudian concepts—that parataxic distortion is but transference, the self-system is character structure and ego psychology and that Sullivan's conception of anxiety is not vitally different from Freud's. It is true that some of the same phenomena are included in both systems. Both men were observing human behavior. Irrational attitudes towards others based on previous relationships first described by Freud and named transference is an observable phenomenon recognized by most people who work with personality problems. The difference between Freud's description and Sullivan's is found in the theory of its development and operation. In the self-system Sullivan certainly describes many phenomena which Freud more mechanistically describes in his concept of the interaction of ego, superego and id in the formation of character traits. Also, the idea that the avoidance of anxiety is the factor underlying the development of defensive systems is an hypothesis held in common by Sullivan and Freud, and certainly one must accord to Freud priority in the formulation of the idea. Thus it is understandable that analysts have thought that Sullivan is saying the same things as Freud. The difference lies precisely in the different theories of personality development, and I think that Sullivan's orientation made it possible for him to observe some things which Freud's system could not include.

Sullivan chose a different name in place of transference because he wished to emphasize the non-sexual origin of the behavior. His definition of parataxic has been described in more detail by others. For purposes of this comparison, I will very briefly define it as the type of thinking, feeling or activity carried on by the young child before he has become aware of the need to communicate precisely with others. Thus a word may have a highly personalized, i.e., autistic, meaning to him. For example, horse to him may mean only a very special dream pony he has imagined as a playmate, and only later he may learn that the name applies to a whole species and that others do not mean his dream pony at all when they use the word. Some of the parataxic mode of thinking remains with us through life especially concerning things not usually discussed with others. Thus a parataxic distortion is a way of reacting to another person in terms of a phantasy of what he is. This phantasy develops out of the person's whole past and represents his highly personalized interpretation of his experiences with significant people. Thus a person may react to all people in authority as if they were severe, forbidding or puritanical if this is the way he experienced his father in childhood. Or he may assume that all people are hostile when it will be found in time that it is his own defensive hostility which he is experiencing. As these distortions become apparent to the person, they tend to disappear. Sometimes this happens because the experience is so obviously different from his conception of it that he, himself, experiences the discrepancy. Sometimes, the inconsistency of his behavior must be repeatedly pointed out to him by another before he is able to become aware of its irrationality. It is apparent that as far as the effect on a person's behavior is concerned, Sullivan is describing what Freud calls transference, but he does not attribute its origin exclusively to the Oedipus situation and he includes character defenses in the term. The strict Freudian does not think of these as transference. Sullivan believed that irrational attitudes could be formed as the result of interaction with all significant people throughout life, the more important influences being the earlier ones.

This leads us to a consideration of the self-system or self-dynamism of Sullivan, as compared with the concept of character as a sublimation of or reaction formation against the instinctual drives of Freud. The Freudian conception is that man becomes an acceptable member of society through modifying his basic drives in the above fashion under the influence of the superego. The Freudian superego represents the introjected attitudes of the culture, especially as experienced through the parents. Sullivan's self is a system or organization of interpersonal processes which are an embodiment or reflection (he uses the term, *reflected appraisals*) of selected attitudes of the culture acquired through contact with the significant people, especially those in authority during childhood. The child lacking the experience and ability to be critical gradually learns through the approval and disapproval of the significant adults what is acceptable behavior on his part. He tends to accept this as the way life is although in fortunate cases he may be able to modify this later. Because of his need for approval, he tends to discard or dissociate aspects of himself which do not meet with approval. Some unapproved aspects of himself may gain access to the self-system through sublimation. Thus the self-system is formed through interaction with people and ends by being an aggregate of the traits approved by the culture—at least as seen through the eyes of the parents. This, or part of it, becomes what the person thinks of as *himself*. All dissociated traits he would tend to deny as belonging to him.

Thus, Sullivan's self-system includes the characteristics described by Freud as belonging to the ego as well as character defenses, and it is formed in a way similar to Freud's description of the formation of character, i.e., by reacting to the incorporated attitudes of the culture, especially as experienced through the parents. The difference again is in the concept of what is dissociated. Sullivan considered that the dissociated was made up of potentialities and behavior which happened to be unacceptable in a particular culture or group or family. Some of these might be unacceptable traits in almost any culture, but in the case of others, there is often a great variation in acceptability from culture to culture or even from parent to parent. Moreover, although sublimation, in the sense of finding an acceptable way of expressing something which would otherwise meet with disapproval accounts for some aspects of the self-system, a great part of the self-system is organized by the process of affirming qualities which meet with approval and discarding those which do not so qualify. Thus, he sees the ego itself as well as its character defenses as being a product of interpersonal relations. This, I think, is not so clearly stated by Freudians, who see character structure as entirely the product of sublimation and reaction formation of instincts, and there is an implication, although it is not specifically stated, that the ego, the reality testing part of the personality, has no specific attributes of its own except an executive function.

Sullivan's concept of primary anxiety seems to me to be a development and amplification of Freud's later theory of anxiety minus the libido aspect. According to Freud, anxiety appears when there is an overwhelming threat of danger to the immature ego. After this first experience, the ego establishes a kind of alarm system in which anxiety appears whenever a similar danger threatens. As a result of this signal of danger, the ego calls out its defenses, and these are symptoms and various other character defenses. In other words, character defenses are a means of avoiding anxiety. It would seem that Sullivan considers the need for security, which, among other things, means avoiding anxiety, the basis of the formation of the self-system. He saw the earliest form of anxiety appearing in the infant before he was fully aware of himself as a separate entity. The earliest feeling is probably one of the loss of a sense of well-being and comes through empathy from the tensions and moods of the mother. Later, the child learns that, by certain activities or inactivities on his part, he can prevent the feeling of discomfort. Thus he tends to choose the activities which produce approval and avoid those bringing disapproval, since disapproval is related to the uncomfortable anxiety feelings. This is very close to Freud's formulation in some respects. Freud defines the nature of the threat to the immature ego as fear of loss of the love of the one who feeds one. It seems clear that both men are describing similar things, but Sullivan's theory gives a more graphic picture of the way anxiety is actually avoided by doing the acceptable thing because of being sensitive to the attitude of another person or group.

Finally, Sullivan includes in his theory a formulation of secondary anxiety which is different from Freud's. Freud defines secondary anxiety as a signal that an old danger threatens. He believed the patient's problem was due to the fact that the signal is automatic and does not take into account that, in the meantime, the patient's ego may have become strong enough to face danger. Since the defense system goes into effect as soon as the signal is given, the more adult ego does not get an opportunity to test its strength. Sullivan has an entirely different conception of secondary anxiety. He believed it is produced by the rigidity of the self-system. The ego has really not become more mature, because part of it has become immobilized, frozen into a rigid pattern formed in the first place to avoid anxiety. That is, the ego is not hidden away somewhere behind the defensive system unspoiled as Freud's theory implies; it has itself become crippled by the defense system and not until this rigidity has been broken down, in other words, not until the self-system has been modified and becomes more flexible can it face new dangers constructively. But this disturbing of the self-system is itself anxiety-provoking since it was formed in the first place as a means of gaining approval, and, therefore, there is resistance to change. This produces the character rigidity of the neurotic. This, I think, Sullivan has described more clearly than others.

Part of the difficulty in seeing where Sullivan and Freud differ consists of the fact that apparently some people unconsciously read into Freud things they have learned from Sullivan (or Fromm or others). It is also possible to reformulate ideas of Sullivan back into Freudian language, as I have just done, and thus make it appear that Freud said the same thing. This is frequently done without taking into consideration the basic differences in theory of personality and the basic difference between the consideration of the individual as an isolated entity and human behavior as the result of the action of interpersonal forces.

So what is the answer to the statement that Sullivan has said the same things as Freud in different words? Sullivan is greatly indebted to Freud. He undoubtedly stands on Freud's shoulders. It is apparent that most of the concepts of the two were attempts to formulate similar phenomena observed, and, in a crude way, they can be translated into each other's language. But to do so is misleading in that it overlooks the basically different orientation of the two men, and it is this very difference in orientation that has made it possible for Sullivan to add certain new ideas to psychoanalysis. Freud seeing man more mechanistically, more as an isolated entity in the universe and primarily evolving as a product of his sexual development, was handicapped by his very theory in incorporating many observations he actually made of man's dependency on the approval of his fellow man. Sullivan, by discarding the cumbersome libido concept, was freer to observe the results of the powerful socializing forces on personality. Moreover, Sullivan does much less unverifiable theorizing than Freud. In short, I believe that although Sullivan's thinking is an outgrowth of psychoanalytic thinking and although he is greatly indebted to Freud, he has opened up a new avenue of approach which makes further research into the study of the human personality more possible.

CHAPTER IV

*SULLIVAN AND TREATMENT**

MARY JULIAN WHITE
Washington School of Psychiatry

I am indebted to Dr. Dexter Bullard and Dr. Otto Will, editor, for quotations from Dr. Sullivan's Chestnut Lodge talks; to Dr. Robert Kvarnes for material from his recorded case seminar; to the Washington School of Psychiatry and Dr. Otto Will, editor, for excerpts from the "Psychiatric Interview" lectures; to Dr. Janet Rioch for her notes on technique; and to the following colleagues who gave liberally of their time and recollections: Drs. Dexter Bullard, Rex Buxton, Mabel Cohen, Robert Cohen, Ralph Crowley, Edna Dyar, Frieda Fromm-Reichmann, Thomas Harris, Robert Kvarnes, Eugene Meyer, Douglas Noble, Edward Ohaneson, Jane Pearce, David Rioch, Janet Rioch, Alfred Stanton, Herbert Staveren, Clara Thompson, Philip Wagner, Edith Weigert, Mabel Wilkin, and Otto Will.—Mary J. White.

O^N THE master's wall at Rugby is an inscription which reads, "This stone commemorates the exploit of William Webb Ellis who, with a fine disregard of the rules of football as played in his time, first took the ball in his arms and ran with it, thus originating the distinctive feature of the Rugby game. A.D. 1823." It was Sullivan's "fine disregard" of the rules of classical psychoanalysis that led to his signal contribution, his capacity to see his way through to one operational statement that covered so vast

* I have inserted in brackets some phrases in the quotations from Sullivan with the hope of making the latter more intelligible.—The Editor.

an area. His insistence on viewing psychopathology as arising out of and living on in the field of interpersonal relations was an enormously useful step.

Sullivan conceived of the person's "self-system" and his "security operations" as developing in response to anxiety in an interpersonal field. That Sullivan was talking about a dynamic form of ego psychology has not been recognized because of his terminology. Freud's *intra-psychic* and Sullivan's *inter-psychic* conflicts are, after all, problems of the same "psyche"; but to communicate the relationship requires the construction of a superordinate system that can incorporate the overlapping descriptive and operational concepts. With knowledge and understanding of both Freud's and Sullivan's formulations, it is possible to recognize the importance of Sullivan's place in the course of psychiatric history. His ideas fit in with the past, with what is going on currently, and, I surmise, with the future of psychiatric thought.

To appreciate Sullivan's practical approach to treatment requires familiarity with his theoretical formulations and also knowledge of the man. He seemed to be animated by a ceaseless concern to learn all that he could about the patients who heretofore had been considered the least accessible to psychoanalysis, namely, the schizophrenics and obsessional neurotics. His transpersonal goal seemed to be the pursuit of anxiety in all its forms, but he was especially interested in the manifestations of it in these particularly difficult cases. His compassion for them stemmed from identification and from the helplessness and hopelessness of the strictly classical analytic approach. His intuitions became important contributions because he worked so hard to communicate them in operational terms and to validate them with others.

His preoccupation with schizophrenia and obsessional neurosis led the way to the inclusion of these most instructive forms of psychopathology within the data examinable by the dynamic psychiatrist. Since he was exploring fields that he did not consider to be accessible by classical techniques, he necessarily developed methods which differed from those found more suitable for other types of patients. It must be noted that Sullivan intended his theories of anxiety and interpersonal process to have general application, but he did not expect his practical approach to the treatment of obsessional and schizophrenic cases to be applied to diverse types of patients.

Sullivan's treatment of these patients stems logically from his recognition of the significance of anxiety in interpersonal relations and in the doctor-patient relationship in particular. He taught that the therapist is always involved in the patient's security operations, by which he meant the patient's efforts to avoid, minimize and conceal anxiety from the therapist, from himself and from others. He said that "skill therefore addresses itself to circumventing these security operations without increasing their scope; this amounts to avoiding unnecessary provocation of anxiety without, however, missing data needed for a reasonably correct assessment of the problem." [1]

To make this clearer, I am going to give several quotations from his Chestnut Lodge talks: "Anxiety is linearly descended from the drops in euphoria which occur in very early life in connection with the disturbances in the significant people around the infant. Anxiety is an experience which signalizes threat to the success one is having with significant adults, or to one's self-respect, which is actually an elaborate structure of reflected respect from others . . .

"Anxiety may in a certain sense be regarded as a sign by which alertness is focussed on a threat to security. We may clear our minds of the notion that the common manifestation of anxiety is the anxiety attack, and realize that the common manifestations are so promptly effective in deflecting the action in a situation that they are scarcely noticed. Until we realize that *that* is the anxiety that's always under foot, we shall be rather at sea about making sense in discussing anxiety in treatment. The effects of anxiety, without [the person's] having noted the preced-

[1] The quotations in this lecture which are taken from unpublished transcriptions of some of H. S. Sullivan's lectures, etc., are published here with the permission of the William Alanson White Psychiatric Foundation. See copyright page.

ing event, are easily susceptible of rationalization. Unless one can get the patient to see—and unless the therapist can see—the occurrence of anxiety followed by a change, one can waste a vast amount of time listening to rationalizations, speculations and problems being used as security operations . . .

"There is bound to be anxiety, and in fact the anxiety probably serves as pain and tenderness do in physical diagnosis, being used by the doctor as a guide to the outlining of diseased areas. The experience of anxiety is always unpleasant, and to avoid the unpleasantness—the pain—one seeks for an anesthetic. There is the anesthetic which comes from selective inattention, the prompt veering away from risky things at the warning of anxiety. There is the anesthetic which has the effect of a hammer-blow, the patient responding with fury at his anxiety, as a result of which he doesn't know quite what did go on. The security that the patient gets in the process of going through unnumbered minor insecurities, and the security which is communicated by the clarity and presumable correctness of the physician's operations are what the patient is there for. As that is assembled, the occurrence of anxiety going on and on in the therapy is nonetheless understood to be a function of the therapy. Once the patient has caught on to the fact that you proceed from anxiety-provoking situation to anxiety-provoking situation, he may say, 'Well, I'm still having a bad time with the doctor, but I'm doing very much better with so-and-so, and so-and-so, and so-and-so in the outer world' In other words he has lost some of the things that made him helpless . . .

"It requires hundreds of repetitions for the patient to catch on to the fact that he can actually express savage views to the doctor and learn something from it. This eternal re-experiencing of anxiety as a threat to progress takes many repetitions, but each repetition is perhaps microscopically less severe. Most anxiety works so well that it is not a clear ingredient of awareness; it's just a little warning which is immediately followed by anger, and various other security operations of which the patient *is* aware. But the preliminary flicker of anxiety hasn't been noticed; that's forgotten; it's gone. The obsessional neurotic, for example, doesn't very often experience anxiety. We may call these persons intensely defensive; it may be easy to think that they have a lot of anxiety but it takes a great deal of educational effort on your part to get *them* to discover that they have any. In general, it's easy to get people to talk about anxiety, but often it's just a word until one has gone to considerable trouble to get the patient to discover what you're talking about. There are, of course, the people who have attacks of anxiety, and who get frightfully anxious, obviously very tense and uncomfortable. I think they are the minority; that is, they're less than half of the people who are apt to show up for a psychiatrist's treatment . . .

"The very nature of anxiety makes it a central problem of psychotherapy. Not that anxiety is not 'normal,' but it is the sign by which the presence of problems, one after another, is always indicated. It is an indicator so unpleasant to the victim that he is quite willing to pass up experiencing it. Thus one must really teach people to recognize the minor grades of anxiety that provoke complicated behavior, symptomatic acts." [2]

In his Psychiatric Interview Lectures Sullivan introduced his concept of the psychiatrist as a *participant observer* in the situation of intercommunication with the patient. The meaning of human actions cannot be deduced by intellectual operations without any past background. The psychiatrist's understanding of the interaction stems from his own past experience, the proscriptions of the culture, and so on. He said: "The facts are that we cannot make any sense of the motor movements of another person except on the basis of meaningful behavior that we have experienced or seen done under circumstances in which its purpose, or at least the intentions behind it, were communicated to us. The therapist has an inescapable involvement in all that goes on in the interview; and to the extent that he is unconscious or unwitting of his participation in the interview, to that extent he does not know what is happening." [3] Sullivan taught that the psychiatrist must be alert to the minor movements of anxiety in himself as well as in the patient. Anxiety in the therapist might

[2] These quotations from Sullivan are taken from unpublished material. See copyright page.

[3] This quotation from Sullivan is taken from unpublished material. See copyright page.

have reference to some foreseen development, something that might happen in the therapy; it might also refer to his own failure to approximate an "ideal" therapist, or to the fact that he might be needing the patient as a source of reflected esteem. Sullivan used anxiety as the sign by which the presence of problems is revealed in the countertransference as well as in the transference. For instance, recognizing that anger is so frequently a sign of incipient anxiety, he cautioned that a therapist who feels actual anger or irritation at a patient needs psychotherapeutic help himself.

In addition to his concept of participant observation, he taught that the interview situation must have the quality of an expert-client relationship. Again I quote from the Psychiatric Interview lectures: "The interview is set up as an expert-client relationship, and the patient must experience something that impresses him as really expert capacity for handling him. When it comes to what you think of as 'expert handling,' if you will pause to consider the people whom you look upon as 'understanding,' that is, able to handle you expertly, you will notice that there is demonstrated by them a very considerable show of respect for you. Meeting such a person can be a really significant event; it is almost a privilege to have him around. You are well managed primarily when you are treated as worth the trouble, and secondarily when the person is keenly aware of disturbances in your feeling of personal worth while in his presence, in other words, disturbances in your security. When he sees that a certain question is going to touch on a topic which will make you feel insecure or anxious, he makes a little preliminary movement which assures you that he is quite aware of the unpleasantness that will attend this question, but that also it is obviously necessary that he should know the information; in other words, he gives you a little warning to brace yourself. Now and then he recognizes that you are having emotions, and possibly anxiety about something which to the doctor seems to be among the most natural things on earth; and at that time he perhaps comes in and says, 'Well, do you feel that that's unusual?' or something like that; and you say, 'Well, yes, doctor, I'm afraid I do,' and he says,

'Dear me, why, I never heard anybody talk honestly who didn't mention that,' and so on." [4]

To Dr. Sullivan, tonal variations in the voice were frequently very dependable clues to shifts in the communicative situation. He also was alert for other slight manifestations of anxiety, such as a change of subject, or not comprehending what the analyst has said, or a question that did not bring a response.[5] He recognized the self-system as an opponent of therapy, in that it has been developed to go "out of touch" at certain times to avoid trouble. His technique was to pursue the particular area in which the change had been noticed, so he would ask the patient to try to recall what had gone through his mind just before the change. If available, he would ask the patient to bring his associations to the point. The rationale of this was quite clear. The self-system would bring in a security operation in order to avoid an anxiety-laden area. Therefore the thoughts occurring just before the introduction of the security operation were crucial, and if one could get an account of them, one would have some information about the patient's anxiety which would be quite reliable. Now, quite often one could not get that sort of information, at least not on the first attempt, but one could teach the patient to pay more attention himself to those crucial points of change. Thereafter, with the patient directing a little more attention, and the doctor a great deal more attention, to those areas, the answer could be obtained. There is nothing vague about using tonal changes of the voice, change of subject, inability to follow a thought, and so on, as a signal to the therapist, and later as a signal to the patient, that something is going on outside of awareness that needs to be investigated.

In the interview lectures he illustrated the importance of tonal changes in the voice by the following example: "If somebody is attempting to tell you what the business of a journeyman electrician is, things may go on quite well until he is on the verge of

[4] This quotation from Sullivan is taken from unpublished material. See copyright page.

[5] For further details about Sullivan's method of dealing with these things, see Dr. Stanton's paper.—The Editor.

saying something about the job which pertains to a field in which he has been guilty of gross disloyalty to his union, at which time his voice will sound altered. He may still give you the facts about what his journeyman electrician should be and do, but he will sound different in the telling. A great part of the experience which one slowly gains takes the form of showing mild interest in this point at which there is a tonal difference. Thus one would perhaps say, 'Oh yes, and the payment of two percent of one's income to this fund for the sick and wounded is almost never neglected by good union members, I gather'; to which the other might reply, again sounding quite different from what he had earlier, 'Exactly. It's a very important part of membership.' And then, if you feel quite sure of the situation, you might say, 'And one, of course, which you have never violated.' Whereupon the other person sounds very different indeed, perhaps quite indignant, and says, 'Of course not!' If you are extremely sure of the way things go, you might even say, 'Well, of course you understand that I have no suspicion about you, but your voice sounded odd when you mentioned it, and I couldn't help wondering if it were preying on your mind.' At this he may sound still more different, and say, 'Well, as a matter of fact, early in my journeymanship I actually did pocket a little of the percentage, and it has been on my conscience ever since.' And the business moves along." [6]

With obsessional patients Sullivan devoted the first few interviews to the taking of a detailed history. He did this in part in order to get a problem for therapy outlined early in the work. He felt it is unfortunate for a patient to feel that more was promised than is obtainable. So, at the end of the initial interviews, he would make a simple, comprehensive and very clear statement of what he had heard at the beginning of therapy. He knew that the patient would not grasp anything like the implications that might seem self-evident. But the statement was gotten in early and had a much less confused part in the orienting of the therapeutic situation than would be the case if it were done piecemeal here and there after distorted phenomena had ap-

[6] This quotation from Sullivan is taken from unpublished material. See copyright page.

peared and escaped observation. He also advised therapists to
"take stock" repeatedly throughout the work, asking themselves
"Where are we now, and what have we still to strive for?" Since
the obsessional state is a way of integration with another person,
he was aware of the danger that the analyst and the patient
might go on becoming more and more obsessional together. For
this reason he emphasized the need to define the goals of therapy
in each case and to keep them always in mind.

Sullivan also used the initial interviews to teach the obsessional patient to begin to recognize anxiety. He spoke on this
interview technique as follows: "In the process of the patient's
unfolding of his story, you will be able, if you listen alertly, to
see again and again where he has had to veer off onto something
collateral or could not proceed in a logical development of a
topic. Such activities are manifestations of anxiety. It is probable
that the patient is scarcely aware that he has shifted. Therefore,
at one point I may say to him, 'Well, you know, I notice you
started telling me so-and-so, and then for some reason you got
to talking about so-and-so. Have you any idea how it happened?'
The patient, remembering it, may do one of two things; he may
burst [out] with rationalizations, in which case I realize there's
too much anxiety here to be brushed aside by a stranger, or
he may be very much struck by the thing and show a little
tendency to inquire. Whereupon I come right in and say, 'Now
I had anticipated your going on to develop such-and-such ideas'
—attempting to say what I'm quite sure was the developmental
outcome of the original stream of thought. If the patient is then
quite anxious, the chances are that I more or less hit it. The
opportunity now for paving the way for good therapy is immense,
because here he is having anxiety. I arranged the situation in
which the anxiety occurred by duplicating and extending the
process that had actually occurred between us a few minutes
before. I can then say, 'Well, I gather you're anxious. You're
uncomfortable. You're worrying about what I think?—or what?'
I'm getting him to talk about his mental state, that is, to bubble,
as it were, some of the vocal tags that seem to discuss his uncomfortable mental state, during which his uncomfortable mental
state gets better, of course. At the end of it I can say, 'Well, this

is an interesting experience of how anxiety works, isn't it? As long as you were able to leave the dangerous thought, you scarcely noticed that you were anxious for a moment. But if the thing is thrust squarely in your face, you know what we mean by anxiety. I can tell you now a little bit more about the question of solving your problem. If there are considerations in the future, visible to you, which seem to justify undergoing a good deal of this very unpleasant experience you've had in the last two or three minutes, rather than to go on as you have been living, then I can conceive of nothing that would prevent your cure. There's nothing essentially ingrained or inborn about your problem, which arises out of your early experience, but we can't take your experience into the shop and fix it. It has to be fixed in you, by you, and there'll be a lot of anxiety connected with the process. If something makes that worth undergoing, okay. If it doesn't, it won't happen.'" [7]

In a further attempt to get around the defenses against anxiety, Dr. Sullivan would hear an obsessional's detailed account of an incident; then, cutting all the preambles and how it came about and so on, he would say, "In such and such a situation you found yourself entertaining such and such thoughts?" [8] It usually was the nub of the story. Then, instead of analyzing what it meant, he would investigate how it was used, when, and for what need.

He taught that with obsessionals "the psychiatrist plays a very active role in introducing interrogations, not to show that he is skeptical, but literally to make sure that he knows what he is being told. Few things do the patient more good than this very care on the part of the doctor to discover exactly what is meant. Almost every time that one asks, 'Well, do you mean so-and-so?,' the patient is a little clearer on what he does mean. And what a relief it is to discover that the true meaning is anything but what he at first says." [9] For example, one patient described nail-biting as an expression of anxiety. Dr. Sullivan acted

[7] This quotation from Sullivan is taken from unpublished material. See copyright page.

[8] Quoted from Sullivan's unpublished material. See copyright page.

[9] Quoted from Sullivan's unpublished material. See copyright page.

puzzled; he wanted to know more about it. By the time the patient had spent five minutes trying to prove that point, the fallacy was apparent. They could agree that it was "acting uncomfortable to impress other people with how uncomfortable they make one." [10]

Sullivan would never interrupt with a request to know what was going on without adding very simply and honestly, "Or have I missed something completely?" He felt it a serious blunder for the therapist to omit the possibility of having missed something. He used to tell students: "The number of times that you have missed something will rather surprise you. It's great news to the patient to find that the doctor *has* missed something; and that the doctor can contemplate such a possibility with equanimity—well, that's even better to know than it is that he can be stupid. Quite often, unfortunately, you haven't missed anything, and your request to know what is going on will have made the patient more uncomfortable. Therefore you must know what the patient might well be working on at this juncture—not necessarily the perfect thing to work on, but something that has recently been before you and has been left untouched. That is the subject that you offer as something that might profitably be attacked." [11]

Sullivan had no use for a "why" question, such as "Why did you do this," because the patient, on the basis of his previous experience, recognizes this as a blame-placing question. He characteristically used circumlocutions or the third person, such as: "One might be curious about the meaning of this information for the relationship with the therapist." [12] Another example—after hearing about some rather humiliating acting-out, he simply said, "Some of the things one does to advertise insecurity do not tend to raise the self-esteem." [13] With obsessionals he might use rather direct, simple statements that would shake the patient up, but for the most part he warned against this. He usually put things in a rather roundabout, hypothetical way, so that some time later

[10] Quoted from Sullivan's unpublished material. See copyright page.

[11] This quotation from Sullivan is taken from unpublished material. See copyright page.

[12] Quoted from Sullivan's unpublished material. See copyright page.

[13] Quoted from Sullivan's unpublished material. See copyright page.

it might come back to the patient and not have to be rejected.

Sullivan would be apt to interrupt expressions of guilt to direct the person's attention to the understanding of what had happened. His stressing the question of what had happened promoted the patient's insight and also implied that he wasn't interested in the question of who was guilty. He did not have any objection to people feeling responsible, but he did interrupt the suffering of irrational guilt.

He was considered to be an active analyst, but not in words. The amount of talking he did and of interpretation he offered were minimal. He knew that his role and his ideas were powerful, and that it doesn't do the patient any service to be swayed. It is so easy to go along with what a leader says is true—without ever discovering that one has known oneself that it is true. He often spoke of the psychiatric risk of "unwarranted interference in other people's lives." Direct intervention was not his privilege, and would only stir rebelliousness.

For instance, a report of the way in which he might try to delay a proposed precipitous marriage is as follows: "I attempt to get the thing under discussion and to get some data, then I quite visibly get disturbed about this. I frown, and I worry, and I give the patient time to realize it. I may even say 'Time out' and get up and leave the room. According to all we know about personality, that means that the patient gets anxious about what I am worried about. Then I say, 'Look, I am not sure that I know what is going on, and I am not sure you are right about what is going on. Is this an important relationship to you? Can't you let it rest awhile?' I have not said anything actually. What with mixing in some dramatics and my questions which practically shout my uncertainty, I hope the patient will realize I have been concerned, but not in any sense mandatory or given to disparaging anybody. I usually try to lay the thing down but say that it puzzles me, 'Is it important to go on with now? I don't know this other person. I am not impressed with your knowing him, and what do you get out of it?' One drifts off to a question that can't be answered but it communicates my doubts." [14]

[14] This quotation from Sullivan is taken from unpublished material. See copyright page.

Dr. Sullivan's interventions included occasional well-timed sighs, grunts, even snorts, and there was a very familiar "a-ha." He taught that with obsessional patients the doctor could be permitted the witting, carefully timed use of any mood suited to the situation except frivolity. He also "used" expressions of anger or mild irritation effectively, cautioning students that the psychiatrist—the expert in such things—might not really be angry with the patient—who is inexpert and thus at a disadvantage. At times with an obsessional patient he might act as though falling asleep, whereupon the patient might say, "How do you expect me to talk to you?" He would retort, "Mr. So-and-so, have you been listening? Have you any idea what you were saying?" The well-considered answer usually had to be "None whatsoever," for Dr. Sullivan was very alert to obsessional movements away from the theme under discussion.

It must be noted that some of these interventions would be repressive if applied to unsuitable cases. Sullivan did not intend to have his practical therapeutic ideas applied to diverse patients. He taught that the psychiatrist's special skill shows in his innate sense of timing and in his choice of passive or active role at particular junctures in appropriate situations.

Sullivan gave up the use of free association after having carefully used the method for a number of years. He continued to emphasize the importance of fleeting, marginal thoughts. He found free association unsuitable for schizophrenics, and learned that obsessional neurotics could use it indefinitely to avoid dealing with anxiety-laden material. He was primarily interested in the areas wherein the patient manifested anxiety; and in an attempt to catch the distortions he would use directed associations. Thus he would often say, "If the mind doesn't bring it, well— let's see what it does bring; perhaps it has something—" Insofar as possible he wanted the communication expressed in terms that could be consensually validated. With obsessional neurotics he traced the deep-seated, primitive forms of anxiety but did not use primitive terms. He applied in his practice phenomenal intuitive knowledge of the material that is outside of awareness, obtaining clues from fantasy content, dreams and symbolic material. Since he felt one could get lost in the maze of symbolic figures, he tended not to interpret dreams as presented; after hearing the associations, he would give the "gist" of the dream in simpler terms, and then again would hear what the patient had to say.

Activity was not manifested by Sullivan in every hour. There might be long periods of work with little intervention. He taught this also, as follows: "If a patient is talking and you don't quite know what he is talking about, and yet at the end of an hour you have a sense that he is getting somewhere, leave him alone. But if you have no sense that he is getting somewhere, you may say, 'Somehow I don't believe that I follow today—I can't see where we've gone—perhaps you can make it clearer next time.'" [15]

In general he controlled the therapeutic situation by movements, questions, and minimal interpretation. He did not let the person flounder indefinitely, and thus ultimately humiliate himself. He knew full well that his interpretations might be wrong and he hoped the patient would correct them. He gave priority in interpretation to the patient's security operations, particularly those protecting against anxiety in the interaction with the psychiatrist. This therapeutic procedure was pointed out by Freud, and Sullivan's operational conceptions have added greatly to the understanding of it. Sullivan also tried to offer two or more alternative interpretations at the same time, thus freeing the patient of the necessity of pleasing the therapist.

In the gradual unfolding of the patterns of living that led to difficulties in living, he advised working first with the peripheral field, the more innocuous people. Then when the patterns had been developed, he would guide the patient to the "me-you" relationship and the demonstration of parataxic distortions. The way he uncovered a distortion was often as follows: the patient might, for instance, have referred rather heatedly to "that day when you called me skinny." Dr. Sullivan would bristle perceptibly and say, "I beg your pardon?," rather sternly. The patient then would repeat and dilate upon the original statement, sounding even more aggrieved. Whereupon Dr. Sullivan would say, "I distinctly recall what I said, namely, that you seemed to have

[15] This quotation from Sullivan is taken from unpublished material. See copyright page.

suffered your mother's opinion that you were thin." With this he dropped it. His patients experienced these incidents acutely, and quickly learned to see what had gone on. He used to say that as soon as the patient has recognized and accepted one parataxic distortion there is hope for a successful outcome of therapy.

Sometimes he seemed obtuse; he just "wouldn't see" a point, or he would make what seemed to be a provocative false statement, designed to be corrected. He knew that the need to correct overrides a good many of the anxieties which sometimes hold up insight. He tried to find the soft spot in the defense system and would push on that. It was of no use to make a frontal attack on anxiety, such as would occur in or result from tackling a strong defense mechanism. For instance, he taught that one cannot analyze male impotence or frigidity in women directly; a tangential approach is necessary.

The negativistic or dominating patient will try to use the analytic situation as a battleground, since he feels better integrated when fighting. The patient may announce that "he will not change" or "doesn't have to." Dr. Sullivan would cut the ground out from such an attempt at battle by a rather dispassionate discussion of the phenomenon of "change," thus: "As far as we know, change seems to be a property of nature. All organisms undergo more or less rapid forms of change. It is therefore not at all a question of whether one will or will not change, since one is doing so all the time. Rather, it is a question of the speed and the direction of change. All that one can hope for in analysis is that one will change in a happier direction as soon as one can, although it will naturally take time." [16]

Dr. Sullivan realized that the patient's capacity to resist too rapid change can be of great value to the analysis. If the long-established and smoothly-functioning system of defenses were to break down too soon, a state of panic might supervene. He would reassure the patient by affirming that they both should have a very real respect for his defenses. If he sensed that marked discouragement and depression had immediately followed a period of rapidly developing insight, he would interpret the discourage-

[16] This quotation from Sullivan is taken from unpublished material. See copyright page.

ment to the patient as a self-protecting measure used in the service of the anxiety created by the threatened change. The rapid change made him feel that he was getting out on a limb, and it is important that he realize the degree of this anxiety. A correct interpretation of this helps to dispel the "use" of the discouragement as a defensive maneuver.

The positive aspects of a situation were given careful attention. After hearing a patient berate his wife at length, he would insist on hearing in addition what the patient liked about her. He wanted perspective, and would follow with questions until the patient could see that much of the derogation did not properly belong to his wife. Similarly with the patient's life story, he spent much time on the development of the areas in which there had been greater success in living. Patients were not allowed to glide over their assets.

He often saw where the patient was going with a pattern of thought before the patient could recognize it. This he might indicate, gesturally or with his gentle "a-ha." One patient described this as follows: "I would suddenly become aware of a change in him, like the alertness of a pointer who has spotted a bird. It was a certain wave of thoughtful, kindly alertness, totally non-verbal. That knowledge of his already being where I didn't know where I was going, made it possible for me successfully to go through a number of rough spots." Early in the work with this same patient Sullivan said, "Somehow or other I feel that there is a great deal of chagrin ahead," which made it more bearable as it became apparent. As the work did progress, Dr. Sullivan's interventions were very infrequent but pithy, as follows: "Living is simple. Are you not aware that you have a tendency to complicate it?" or "It takes a great deal of competence to entertain as complex a mental disorder as you do," or "You have copied your mother's paranoid psychosis with some improvements on it." These seemed intolerable because of the close understanding they implied and because of the obligation toward oneself that resulted from such admissions. The patient could, however, approach the problem in somewhat different language and always had Dr. Sullivan's wholehearted support. In another case he pointed out that the patient hadn't set out to be the way he was.

"Was it not actually rather grandiose for one to assume that he could be entirely responsible for being such an evil person? The grandiosity might well be looked at." [17]

He considered it mandatory with schizophrenic and obsessional patients to give positive recognition of a forward move on the part of the patient. Silence is unforgivable at such a time. One should validate it and recognize it before moving on. He described how this might be accomplished thus: "In developing my summary of what has been achieved, I try to pluck out highlights from the associational train that give a feeling of continuity and progress toward the goal that I wish to talk about. I think it would be quite worth while to reserve two or three minutes at the end of a profitable hour to recall to the patient that for perhaps twenty minutes of this hour there was apparent indifference to the warnings of anxiety, thought following thought with amazingly little concern about what impression it would make or what it might mean. And I may say to the patient—'it is from this stream of thought which you had for about twenty minutes that we picked up this material which has made such excellent sense.'" In his teaching of this point he continued: "I'm willing to use considerable interpretative ingenuity to demonstrate to the patient that there *has* been a forward move when I'm pretty sure that it has occurred. If the patient is quite sick, he may be exceedingly grateful for discovering that something has at last started, even if he must at first perceive it through your eyes, ears, and mouth instead of through his own observation. If you, however, from an excess of zeal, mistake something for progress, and rub it into the patient, he will be so angry at you for your stupidity and optimism that some of his unrecognized emotional problems are apt to show, for which one can also be deeply thankful." [18]

At times, Dr. Sullivan would give reassurance when a patient seemed to be mulling along without apparent progress. He described his way of handling this as follows: "I say quite simply

[17] The quotations from Sullivan in this paragraph are taken from unpublished material. See copyright page.

[18] The quotations from Sullivan in this paragraph are taken from unpublished material. See copyright page.

that I have definitely a feeling that something is in progress, that I cannot guess what, and I can quite understand the patient's feeling puzzled, but I suggest that we struggle along as is for the time being. That's all the patient needs. If he has received the assurance that this is not a hopelessly befogged area, he will plug along somewhat better. Before very long something usually appears which one can see in retrospect required a lot of preparation, so that concepts rather remote and quite thoroughly misunderstood by the patient could finally be communicated; whereupon I beam and say, 'Well, don't I hear you saying so-and-so?' —and the patient says, 'Good God, I think so.' Then I remember that this has been a hard pull, and I say, 'Well, perhaps we are now getting the returns on this very obscure effort. Let's go right ahead now, and we may even come to see why the effort itself was necessary.' Occasionally it is possible in the course of the next two or three hours to get a sketchy feeling of understanding of some of the obscure things that were dealt with. Sometimes the patient sees through it before you do, and explains it. If the patient doesn't, and I have a pretty fair hunch, I rather like to toss it out, again sort of conversationally at the end of the hour, because it's vital, according to my lights, that the patient come gradually to share my conviction that the personality system will disentangle itself if it gets a chance. Any evidence that such a tendency is at work, and some clue as to how it's working, really gives the personality quite a hand. It's a great encouragement to the patient." [19]

Dr. Sullivan's attitudes toward expressions of positive feelings were several. He said: "When I feel that a patient is developing an appreciation for me, I have to think of another aspect of such things. Can this patient afford to appreciate me this much? If a person has a tenuous self-esteem what is the cost of thinking the doctor is wonderful? It is something he can't stand. He has worth only because this wonderful person is interested in him. Alas, I have too many things to do to keep up such a relationship, and as these indications of high regard come forth, I ask very blunt questions. I can with safety inquire, 'Well, do I seem different

[19] This quotation from Sullivan is taken from unpublished material. See copyright page.

from other people?' Or if the patient is moved to say that he has found it easy to talk to me, I should be inclined to say, 'What the hell, it is your first venture.' This indicates that I am not having any miracles, and he has not made a fool of himself with me. However, when a patient expresses appreciation for something that has really been valuable to him—that is a ticklish emergency. If one does not acknowledge commendation from a patient, he may think you are too big for him. So I thank him for his kind words and then get on with something else. The risk is that it may go over so big that he thinks he has to give me plenty. Therefore I need to have an idea of what I want to investigate, and after acknowledging the very kind sentiment, I say, 'And how are we coming along with so-and-so to the problem?' Just that simple." [20]

One patient, after about nineteen attempts, had succeeded in correcting a major fiction that he had been peddling all his life. At the end of the hour he mentioned a wave of warm feeling for Dr. Sullivan, who simply said: "Yes, when one corrects a major fiction in the presence of another person, one is apt to have a warm feeling for that person." [21]

Sullivan summarized his therapy of obsessional neurosis thus: "Under great stress, which the obsessional dynamism is not able to handle, the person who has put the principal dependence on obsessional processes will develop schizophrenic phenomenology. The indication, therefore, is not to apply too much pressure to an obsessional patient in the area where he can't stand it. The obsessional processes are devices for providing an uncomfortable approach to security. Until the interpretation of a particular life situation is almost self-evident, there is no use offering interpretation to an intensely obsessional person. If the doctor doesn't get in the patient's way, the context is run through the mill, and each time it becomes a little clearer. That's the way that obsessional personalities seem to heal themselves. They run their security operations over and over and over, but not entirely with-

[20] This quotation from Sullivan is taken from unpublished material. See copyright page.

[21] This quotation from Sullivan is taken from unpublished material. See copyright page.

out the rest of the personality achieving something in the process. Every now and then, about the time that you feel certain that you can make the interpretation and that there is no possibility of its being befogged, the patient beats you to it. At other times you offer your interpretation, somewhat like propounding a riddle, 'Well, now, actually doesn't this picture which you depicted mean so and so? What else can it mean? I can't find any other hypothesis that accounts for the course of events.' Then, with pretty severe anxiety, the patient gives some faint indication of agreement and rapidly gets himself to say, 'Well, why in the world did it take us so long?,' or words to that effect. That is the type of approach to the hurdle and falling over it that seems to constitute the therapy of the obsessional neurosis." [22] A close relationship between the obsessional dynamism and schizophrenic process was postulated by Dr. Sullivan, for occasionally he had observed a fairly easy transition from one state to the other, rather late in the patient's life.

Sullivan's understanding of obsessional fears should be mentioned. These are frequently of doing some violence, of assaulting sexually, or the fear may be that one will jump out of a window. Sullivan taught that it is helpful to call attention in a very matter-of-fact way to the "obsessional" or "compulsive" nature of these fears, then to go on to indicate that one keeps on busily plaguing himself with such thoughts in order to distract one's attention from unwelcome, repressed conflicts which would otherwise come into awareness. The patient's insistence that these are very imminent dangers can be met with the statement that they have to feel imminent in order to be sufficiently distracting.

Expressed fear of insanity is a similar problem. Frequently the patient is reassured if it is pointed out to him that his fear of "going mad" is a fear of loss of control and is related to a feeling of helplessness; that in some people this is expressed in terms of a fear of losing control of the sphincters, in others, a fear of losing their minds. The main problem is to understand the underlying fear of being helpless.

Suicidal ideas in neurotic patients would be met with his

[22] This quotation from Sullivan is taken from unpublished material. See copyright page.

usual investigative, methodical interrogation; starting with "Is this the first time the thought has occurred to you?," he would go on to find out "all about" the early history of it. This demonstrates that he is not particularly disturbed by the present threat; it simply becomes material for analysis.

His response was different with some obsessional neurotics. He once said: "I have encountered pretty vigorous threats of suicide in retaliation for my alleged brutality to obsessional neu- rotics. That has been just an invitation to real brutality. I have asked them not to make it really awkward for me by having to hire scrubwomen to remove the results, and so on. That is liter- ally the way I have reacted, to the point where patients have become quite interested in how beautiful it would be to kill themselves to be even with me for my brutality. Again, I just say to them: 'The analyst as a human being and as a therapist is interested in live people, not dead ones—if one simply has to jump out of a window, it would be more convenient not to do it on the premises.' The patient's fear that he may commit suicide is one of the really impressive fears or phobias that may be the presenting picture in an obsessional neurotic. As soon as I have convinced myself that there is a rather stable obsessional state rather than one of these indefinite obsessional schizoid condi- tions, it has been my practice to treat the matter very roughly, assuming that there is practically no danger. The things that strike me with considerable force as complications are all in the field of schizophrenia." [23]

Sullivan was sensitive to the various implications of weeping. If he felt that the patient was concerned with how badly he felt and was wallowing in woe, he would attack it by mentioning humiliation and the further separation of oneself from people by self-pity. Thus it was either stopped or changed into direct rage at Sullivan. As one patient put it: "It is so much easier to be angry at something that you know that you're angry at than to feel angry and not know what it is." Sullivan seemed to be saying, "As long as you have to fight, I'll fight with you, but let's get it into the open." In contrast to this was his response to what

[23] This quotation from Sullivan is taken from unpublished material. See copyright page.

seemed to be real grief work. If the patient wept, or if the eyes became a little reddened and moist, he would call attention to it. "Did I notice that the eyes became a little moist?" Again he used a very tentative terminology. If there was an indication that the patient really was crying, he would pause and then begin, in a low tone of voice and quite slowly, to comment in a soliloquy about the respectability of weeping. He would go on about the need of doing the grief work in order to separate oneself from the loved object or from the lost objective desire which had been festering, as it were, in the personality from childhood onward. Then he would add: "Now, to make this useful, I need to know what is going on in the mind at the present time, at the present moment." [24] If the patient answered with a definite episode of having lost something—it didn't matter what it was, he may even have lost an illusion, a penknife or have been separated from somebody—then one could be relatively sure that the grief work was in progress. He might not check the weeping for some weeks. Finally he would intervene with "Well, now is it not appropriate to stop grieving and to see what this is all about?" or "Isn't it time now to overcome this, after all, unconstructive grief and to begin to look for what you can do with your productive resources?" He had as much optimistic faith in innate human competence as he had pessimistic awareness of the interference of the self-system with the realization of human competence.

Sullivan was keenly aware of the anxiety-provoking character of envy.[25] "Nothing is so hard to endure, is so security-disrupting, as envy of others." [26] His development of this theme was as follows: "Let us consider a situation in which the analyst has been interested in attempting to get a patient to sort out friendly and unfriendly impulses. We may find that the patient's hostility seems to be poisoning everything, including therapy. Then we

[24] The quotations from Sullivan in this paragraph are taken from unpublished material. See copyright page.

[25] He also noted that it is an outstanding characteristic usually of people in our society, as well as of people in some other places.—The Editor.

[26] This quotation from Sullivan is taken from unpublished material. See copyright page.

may note that he suffers *any* demonstration by another of not only superiority, but of contentment, of peace of mind—anything that *he* doesn't have. He feels as if he must do something about it. He engages in a fantastic amount of manipulating the environment, of wisecracking, disparagement, criticism, and assertions of great power, the upshot of which is that it would be quite proper to jot down that this man's hostility appears in all his behavior. But I still say that, yes, no doubt the hostility stands in the way, but what is it that is eternally calling out these manifestations of hostility? The patient suffers anxiety whenever anything suggests to him that a person is getting along better than he is—in conversation with him, or in anything else. His ordinary response to such suggested superiority is to show that he's better or to show that the other person is worse. As more information comes to light, it becomes evident that the hostility is not really what defeats him. What does defeat him is that he is terribly insecure in the presence of anyone who seems to be doing at all well. Therapeutically, the problem is to concentrate on instances of hostile movements as indices of insecurity; one responds to any particular hostile movement by looking for ways in which the patient felt insecure at that time. The patient needs to see how these ways in which he felt insecure led to an invidious comparison between himself and the other person. The hostile performance is in essence an accelerating spiral of desperate attempts to prop up a steadily undermined security, with the result that the patient is more and more detested and avoided. If, by the most drastic presentation of the profoundness of his insecurity and of his feeling of inferiority, he can be given pause in the acceleration of this spiral, then something useful can begin to happen. If the patient will be alert to how small he feels with anybody who seems to be at all contented or successful in any respect, then he may not have need for this hateful superiority —which is hateful in part because he hates himself so much, being unable to be what he claims to be. Perhaps, too, he can begin to observe some of his actual abilities and gifts, which I am sure he has lost track of under the general pressure of demonstrating that he is better than others. This picture comes not from any primary hostility in the personality in the sense of an outstanding trait inculcated in childhood, *but from a defect of personal worth inculcated in childhood.*

"I think that much of the hostility can be converted into dissatisfaction with oneself, and that is a profitable conversion. That gives one something to work on by the good old logical method of looking for negative instances. Much of the low opinion [of themselves] which people tote around in the world is the result of a skew of attention which has been progressive, such that they give themselves no particular credit for abilities and achievements, and become more and more preoccupied with demonstrating what they don't have, as a result of which they feel more and more imperilled in their prestige and self respect. If they're doing something about *that* that makes the outer world the target in one way or another—either the paranoid system, or all these hostile, aggressive, bedevilling [belittling] techniques and so on—I find it useful to get this back into dissatisfaction with oneself. Then we can look into the natural history of this dissatisfaction, feeling quite certain that the person has assets, and quite certain that many of the liabilities are specious, the result of distorting early influence." [27]

Dr. Sullivan believed that in schizophrenia "the defect of personal worth inculcated in childhood" stems largely from the interaction of the mother and the infant. He recognized genetically determined, constitutional differences between individual newborn infants before the processes of acculturation start, but his attitude seemed to be—why bother about that part, since one would be unable to do anything about it.

From this point on I shall be talking of his treatment of schizophrenia. With catatonics he was gentle in a kindly, reserved way, whereas he treated the paranoid patient with distant and at times cold reserve. He knew that "one cannot fool a schizophrenic," so was outstandingly honest with them. He taught hospital personnel to accept the very sick, regressed patient on an adult level, and to accept the total range of acted-out interests and needs of the patient. One of Sullivan's great contributions

[27] This quotation from Sullivan is taken from unpublished material. See copyright page.

has proved to be his development of "milieu therapy," in which the hospital administration and entire staff are utilized in the therapy of schizophrenic patients. His work along this line at the Sheppard Pratt Hospital has been published.

His own understanding of the anxiety that psychotics experience was somehow communicated to them, so that there was promptly established a relationship that could transcend the anxiety as it arose. The schizophrenic felt immediately he was understood; he had an immediate experience which was achieved by a short-cut approach through identification, a togetherness with which the patient again could dare to face reality. He got the feeling of being understood without anyone's using words, which is enormously important to psychotics. Except by his attitude of kindly reserve, Dr. Sullivan would not reassure them. Reassurance frequently is interpreted by the patient as just the opposite, as "My God, he really thinks I *am* hopeless!"

He himself dared to accelerate the release of tremendous amounts of anxiety in his patients because he could be so supportive and because he could see the field ahead. However, he taught such great caution in the sudden release of anxiety that it has been said that he had an exaggerated idea of patients' frailty. In general, he warned against the therapist's being instrumental in releasing more anxiety than the patient could integrate at any given time, and warned against the release of anxiety in a patient for whom immediate therapeutic help was not available.

His view of schizophrenic process was this: "If one encounters grave conflicts between one's needs for satisfactions and the necessity for feeling secure and free from severe anxiety, long before there has been a consolidation of intimacy with a fellow being—a real other person with all the new interest and refinement which such intimate relations entail—the appearance of marked anxiety will lead to rapid regression. The loss of control of awareness with the eruption into the field of attention of the less refined and specific referential processes—dream thoughts—and revery processes ordinarily ignored—will be followed by a course which quickly eliminates from the manifestations of the self a great part of the recent addition to that self. In other words, there will be a strikingly regressive course in which social habits, communicative utilization of speech, and so on, will be lost very swiftly, and the gross picture of the hebephrenic will manifest itself. The reason that the hebephrenic development appears so promptly in those who have not had this preadolescent experience is presumably that there is nothing of great value which holds them at the height of personality evaluation that they have achieved, such as the experience of human intimacy.

"In contrast with the foregoing, the development differs if there has been a consolidation of experience of a preadolescent character. In other words, if the person before this disaster has experienced the need for and [acquired] novel returns from intimacy with another person, a chum, a friend, then the eventuality of schizophrenic disaster will not follow anything like so swift a regressive divestment of the later acquisitions of personality, but will, instead, follow a course primarily characterized by its close relationship to the nightmares which are experienced by adolescents and some chronological adults. The conflict between the needs for satisfaction and security tipped the threshold of awareness to the point that these processes escaped the excluding devices [of the self] and took the place of referential processes. This has a great deal to do with the very thing we see in troubled dreams, nightmares, and the like, such processes representing the application of rather high orders of revery processes and subverbal or autistic verbal operations in a sustained application to the solution of a problem.[28] As long as that continues the patient may be called catatonic, and at any time the patient may despair, in which case the hebephrenic change supervenes, or the patient may find the paranoid solution."[29]

He described schizophrenics as very shy people, low in self-esteem, and subject to the suspicion that they are not particularly appreciated or respected by strangers. Almost all of them have come to believe that they have very poor judgment about other people, and that if other people seem favorably interested in them, that interest is either fraudulent or due to ignorance of the

[28] Compare Sullivan's discussion of schizophrenic processes in the *Conceptions.*—The Editor.

[29] This quotation from Sullivan is taken from unpublished material. See copyright page.

patient. In other words, the interest will die as soon as the stranger discovers what the patient is like. The more paranoid the tendency, the more the patient will think something is being put over on him. In any case he feels he has exceedingly little ground for the development of trust and confidence in the physician. Sullivan pointed out that the doctor, unless extremely careful, contributes to this, for he is inclined to build on his own experience, and that the introduction of something which the patient does not follow can be hard on the relationship. The patient gets into something like this: "Here the doctor understands something and I can't, so I can't follow him at all, so that proves I am no good." [30]

Sullivan commented further: "Schizophrenics during childhood seem not to have been able to utilize the helpful experience of growing up with a group of juveniles. All children show deficiency in their automatic skill, in areas where they have been denied the conventional opportunity of acquiring it. Thus these patients have had to live a good many of their juvenile motivations in fantasy which could be communicated to no one. They have had to act more adult than they feel at each age level. Unhappily one cannot short-circuit the course of maturation of ability, but one can learn from human example how to act as if more mature. It still leaves the unsatisfied longing and needs for development and experience which the sudden maturation denied. These needs can be discharged only in fantasy and in sleep. It [that is, acting as if one were more mature while expressing one's unsatisfied longings, etc., in fantasy and sleep] makes for avoiding any intimate exchange with others. It is as if what schizophrenics would like to talk about is childish, and also they don't have a grasp of what other people like to talk about. These patients feel childish and really profoundly inferior. They become so careful to conceal this inferiority in preadolescence that it keeps them from the benefits of a close, confidential chum. The cause of their isolation hasn't a ghostly connection with sexual things, but it is bound to have disastrous effects on sexual development. In adolescence they have to be still more skillful in

[30] This quotation from Sullivan is taken from unpublished material. See copyright page.

adjusting their deception to others.[31] That is where the panic of inferiority, loneliness and failure occur. Therapists should avoid galloping into the enormous forest of sexual preoccupations with schizophrenics; it is so much more important that a great deal be done about the business of loneliness." [32]

With mute catatonics Dr. Sullivan carried on slow soliloquies in part of every interview for months, being careful to drop only one idea at a time. He would not make cryptic or ambiguous statements that might be misinterpreted, and he would try to say "all" about any one idea, offering simple, inclusive statements which left no room for misinterpretation. He worked constantly to keep the general level of anxiety at a minimum. He did subtle things, such as warning the person that he was about to speak by some movement, then throat clearing, and then speaking. The idea itself also would be introduced slowly and in gradual crescendo. With a frankly anxious patient he might spend many hours at a time, the implication being "I'll go through this with you; we must get out what makes you so anxious about it." [32]

His method of interrogation and reassurance of an ambulatory schizophrenic patient can best be given in his own words: "One must have a lively plan of action before one attacks the problem of finding out what really worries the patient. One can get good hunches in hearing past history, for the patient can talk about past problems more easily than what he is panicky about now. Finally one may ask the patient, 'What really is haunting you all the time?' Let us suppose the patient says, 'Doctor, I am a homosexual.' What do you do then? You can hear what is said. You can presume it does not mean what you think. You can notice it is extremely important to the patient and you can say something which indicates you have survived the blow; that you don't think it is as awful as he thinks you might think. It is risky

[31] Sullivan's abrupt transitions from discussing the behavior of the mentally ill to their developmental history illustrate, I think, some of his ideas as to the role of the "perduring manifestations" of past experiences in interpersonal relations.—The Editor.

[32] This quotation from Sullivan is taken from unpublished material. See copyright page.

for the patient to think he is homosexual, or know he is homosexual, so the next move has to be as automatic and spontaneous
as 'Now what in the world makes you think so?' The statistically
most frequent response will be 'Well, you know damn well I am,
doctor.' There must not be stuttering or obscure retreats into
asking irrelevant questions. There has to be something done
now which reduces the anxiety. So, as the patient comes back
with 'You know I am homosexual,' I say, 'Well, I don't know
what you mean by being homosexual—it hadn't occurred to me.
What makes you think you are? Do you know anything that
points that way?' And the patient always does. I am trying to put
him on the spot so that he can defend his position. There is no
telling what I will hear. I may hear that he has had 4,572 un-
questionably homosexual entanglements with men. I must still
do something, and what? Suppose I actually did hear about a
homosexual experience, then I would proceed to inquire about
the circumstances. Did he seek it, or was it forced on him, and
so forth—just commonplace inquiries before the final movement.
He may say that he finds himself interested in other people's
genitals and wishes they were interested in his, and feels funny
sensations in his mouth and every time anybody lights a cigarette
he has to rush to the toilet. I must get in now because I want
the last act to work. The last act is when I think I have got
enough, when the person does not seem to be as tense as he was
at the great admission, then I gaze into the future and say, 'Oh,
yes, I can see how it looks that way to you *now*.' Then I am
through. I feel I have done everything I can to meet the risk in
a fashion that will protect my relationship with the patient and
prevent him from going into a panic over now we know he is
homosexual and it is horrible. If something has been said that
does not deny, but which indicates that the patient may be
wrong, I feel that is sufficient. That carries the implication that
we will talk some more." [34]

He continued: "I want to talk a little further about the whole
notion of the awful things that ail schizophrenics. I know no

[34] This quotation from Sullivan is taken from unpublished material. See
copyright page.

reason to believe that schizophrenics are startlingly different from anybody else. It is a matter of the timing of events, and if a person is really repeatedly restricted to sexual relations with members of his own sex only, then in all reasonable probability the therapeutic problem is what blocks his freedom to the other sex, and if a person is convinced that he is an unprincipled scoundrel concerned only with such acts, the problem is what has stopped him from developing beyond that. If a person is schizophrenic or very disturbed over alleged peculiarities of sex life, then the approach to that person, who obviously has not been able to fit into life on an adult pattern, is to find out why he could not get further. Rather than having views about homosexuality, my approach is that it is not the only thing that is making him have difficulty with people; it never is. I want to know all the difficulties one has, as well as the fact that one follows a homosexual pattern of life, and generally there are glaring defects in living. Quite frequently these are closely related to the why and wherefore of the homosexual pattern, but when it comes to disturbed people, I never enter into this business of homosexuality until the patient has accepted it as part of a relatively commonplace problem." [35]

With psychotics Sullivan of course made use of the most primitive form of pregenital material. He seemed to understand it without words. He would observe it and hear it for months until quite sure of his relationship with the patient; then he would change his manner of handling the psychotic communication. He described this change thus: "When the work is going well, I finally run a considerable risk by beginning to be unpleasant and demanding about his horrible thoughts and terrors. I now begin to indicate my disrespect for these things. 'God help us, why must we have this hokum when we are doing useful work most of the time. I know something bothers you, but does it have to be disguised as a catastrophe? These horrible thoughts, do they bring out goose pimples on you? If I encounter anything horrible, I expect goose pimples.' It is a distinct playing down of what is at best lunatic language. I would not dignify the

[35] This quotation from Sullivan is taken from unpublished material. See copyright page.

stuff by asking what he is talking about. I know he does not know. If I can get him to leave the neologistic hoop-la and discover when he began to feel frightened, what was in his mind, we will very much more rapidly discover the formulation of his profound insecurity as to his worth and fitness for human society."

"If I hear some kind of involved business about homosexuality or abattoir fantasies of slashing and tearing, I can surmise these things represent fantasies from an early time when one had completely to inhibit the expression of rage. Kids find it easy to entertain fantasies of taking the axe to troublesome parents and teachers and making a slaughterhouse. One has to be prepared for the eruption of this sort of thing, and probably my response would be, 'Well, hell, you must have felt terribly *sore* sometimes in the past.' That proves that I am not horrified and I don't get in too deep. I have tossed out a lifeline, the awful stuff is before us, and we are still there." [36]

A good many schizophrenics are entirely unpredictable as far as suicide is concerned. Dr. Sullivan approved of Kempf's idea that a good deal of the catatonic operation in a vague sense pertains to death and rebirth. To die in order to be reborn is different from the type of suicide that depressives think of. With a puzzled schizophrenic who was all wound up in the urgent necessity of killing himself, Dr. Sullivan once said, "That is, you want to begin all over"; and the patient gazed at him with clarity and said, "Yes." Whereupon there was an end to the suicidal business.

With less sick but none-the-less panicky patients, Dr. Sullivan might respond to a suicidal threat with a serious discussion of the possible value of these suicidal ideas. A situation which seems unbearable at the moment may be felt to be more bearable as long as one has the knowledge that one can get out of it. Thus an idea that one could at any time commit suicide, actually has the result of carrying one through an otherwise intolerable experience. This formulation acknowledges the difficulties of the patient's actual experience, recognizes his "right" to choose his

[36] This quotation from Sullivan is taken from unpublished material. See copyright page.

course of action, and still indicates in a positive way that seemingly unbearable difficulties can be tolerated.

In supervision Sullivan was at his best in handling the minutiae of the schizophrenic's way of dealing with his fellows. One colleague was working on a patient's recurrent delusion that he was the Assistant Secretary of State. Dr. Sullivan, in a supervisory hour, said, "You know, I think this fellow has the feeling that he has made a fool of himself somewhere." This was worked on and validated by the patient; the delusion did not recur. Another colleague controlled his work with a schizophrenic boy with Dr. Sullivan. After about six months of work, in which there had been no talk of sex matters at all, Dr. Sullivan suddenly said, "You know, I think this man is one of those very unfortunate youngsters who wants to be a woman but cannot be a satisfactory woman because he has a penis, and is very concerned about his homosexuality and his penis's size, and so on." This also later proved to be true. The dynamics of this situation were explained by Dr. Sullivan thus: "From certain parental or family groups, a boy finds all attractive merits in the mother. Sometimes her significance gradually shifts from that which must necessarily inhere in the mothering role to the point where everything that seems to be estimable and good to the boy is an attribute of the mother. The father may be successful in the eyes of the world, but his virtues may be irrelevant to the boy or affect him so unpleasantly that they are not really esteemed at all, no matter what lip service is paid to them. Under those circumstances the pattern of the male is very unattractive and to a certain extent a boy tends to be a woman. That is, he wants to be what seems to him comfortable and decent, and so on, which appears to be personified in the mother. This requires more and more guarding in male society lest one is accepted as a sissy or in some other fashion which is hard on self-esteem. The later clues to the misfortune in models tends to show as a great interest in and much thinking about girls. This can be taken as some [kind of] libido development, but the facts are that this fits in with what one really would like to be. Being female is what one feels suited to be, and good at being, yet it is impossible because of the cultural pressure and accident of sex. One may get so involved in what unhappily has to remain one's private life in contrast to public life, that one has no opportunity to check up on oneself with anyone else because there is so much that must be kept secret. Finally all sorts of homosexual data are acquired without, so far as I know, there being any insurmountable barrier to women, but there is a definitely insurmountable barrier to seeking the *male role* with women." [37]

One of the colleagues has commented that he thought Sullivan the most "all or nothing" therapist that he had known; he showed just plain nerve in what he would do with the schizophrenic. For instance, if a psychotic asked for sex relationship with the therapist, Dr. Sullivan considered saying: "When I want sex experience, I want it with a *person*." Thus with a catatonic Sullivan might start on a tangential approach and then suddenly hit at the center of the whole problem. He could do that because he could be supportive. With a sick schizophrenic he could deal directly with "really where the patient was living," and with that give support by being direct.

With obsessionals as well as with schizophrenics he incited some of the most intense transference reactions and used them therapeutically. He was keenly aware of what the patient had to go through. Sullivan's therapy was a research project dedicated to the development of techniques to help these two types of patients to achieve recovery with durable insight.

The closing of this talk will be in Dr. Sullivan's words. He referred to a speech of Newton Baker in which the latter said, "The outstanding mark of an education is the ability of a person to hold his judgment in suspense on unsettled questions." Dr. Sullivan continued: "If psychiatry were anything like a finished science or art, one might find ample motivation for a long life in it in desiring to be appreciated for the skill with which one distributed the benefits of this to one's fellow man. But psychiatry is very far from such a finished science and art. It is really a great experiment, a great exploration, almost purely research. Even if I could, I don't know whether I should be happy to be appreciated as a great psychiatrist from the standpoint of cures

[37] This quotation from Sullivan is taken from unpublished material. See copyright page.

and the adequate meeting of needs at this stage of our development. Insofar as one lives up to the ideals of benevolent investigation in a very difficult field, to contribute to the ultimate benefit of humanity, it seems to me one has an adequate justification for the career." [38]

[38] This quotation from Sullivan is taken from unpublished material. See copyright page.

DISCUSSION

PHILIP WAGNER

Washington-Baltimore
Psychoanalytic Institute

AFTER Dr. Sullivan's death I became progressively preoccupied with work in Baltimore and have had very few occasions since then to exchange views with my former associates in the Washington school, so that this opportunity is a welcome one. This does not mean that we in Baltimore are isolated from Dr. Sullivan's legacy to psychiatry. You all know that he spent several years doing his initial research at the Sheppard and Enoch Pratt Hospital. When I arrived there in 1937 the memory of Dr. Sullivan was such a pervasive legend that I assumed he must assuredly be dead. I could not imagine then that a living person could be considered with such awe by his contemporaries; and like a legendary figure, now that he is dead, his stature and influence continue to grow.

In referring to Freud or Sullivan on this occasion, I do so in a generic sense. Once removed from our teachers, we cannot speak for them. Even when Dr. Sullivan was alive and I would quote Sullivan to Sullivan, he would more often than not reply, "You do not understand me. Please try again." In the twenty-two sources quoted by Dr. White, I would anticipate twenty-two different slants on Dr. Sullivan. It is my impression that a great teacher always imparts a varying impression on each of his students . . .

Dr. Thompson's historical summary and Dr. White's anthology and Dr. Miller's carte blanche give me very wide latitude. I am selecting two points around which to relate my remarks

151

from these excellent papers: Dr. Thompson's statement that Dr. Sullivan was a psychoanalyst, a point which Dr. White's paper would seem to make incontestable; and Dr. White's reminder that Dr. Sullivan concerned himself with obsessional and schizophrenic patients. As an extension to their remarks, I wish to suggest with some emphasis that we consider Sullivan's contributions as not necessarily a contradiction of basic Freudian theory and practice; not as alternative hypotheses or techniques; but rather as complementary contributions particularly in the areas of his major interests.

I am not in this manner inviting any discussion as to what is a psychoanalyst. I understand that the Committee for the Evaluation of Psychoanalytic Therapy of the American Psychoanalytic Association has been considerably delayed in its work, being unable to achieve any consensus among the members as to what constitutes psychoanalysis. This is a curious aspect of our profession. We spend the year trying to decide with our patients who they are and then spend our time at national meetings trying to decide who we are.

It has been frequently emphasized that Sullivan's contributions had to be made in a frame of reference other than the instinctual theory and that he found it necessary to create a terminology which related to the reference which he emphasized: that man was inextricably a part of the social fabric, even from the very beginning, and that the conduits and form of his expression were not preordained but were reactive to the needs of others. *His abjuration of psychoanalytic orthodoxy was therefore sharp and sometimes militant.* He had something to say aside from and in addition to classical psychoanalytic formulations and technique. He would not attenuate his views by fitting them into a framework of an already established formalized system. The very conception of a *system* was unacceptable. A system of therapy tends to stifle research, ingenuity, intuition. It can become therapy by imitation. One does not apply a system to a schizophrenic. Even in so-called orthodox psychoanalysis it is unlikely and undesirable that any stereotyped approach be considered inviolable. Each therapist achieves his own methods for adapting techniques to the patient's needs, and the particular techniques consistently found useful in dealing with a hysteric would be catastrophic if applied to the schizophrenic; the more narcissistic the neurosis the less applicable any formalized technique.

Let us consider once again the libido theory, overworked by the classical analyst, and rejected by Sullivan, as it may apply in a case of obsessional neurosis, from the point of view as to whether Sullivan's interpersonal formulations invalidates the older theory.

The essential, oversimplified Freudian formulation would be that anal erotism—anal libido—becomes entangled in the struggle with the parents; that the child reacts to frustration and denial of anal pleasures with obstinacy, rebellion, and rage; later contains these attitudes by reaction formation: abhorrence and disgust with anal interest and a masochistic diffidence and compliance as a mask for the unacceptable earlier sadistic rebellious reactions.

Sullivan would say that the impact between child and mother, in which the mother uses her own anxiety, guilt, disgust, and affection to civilize the child, results in a need to parry such intimidation and rejection. The child uses the anal arena to play out the issue with the parent. The child's choice of his anality is a product of a parent-culture attitude to anal activity at a time when response to the parent is limited to very few personal functions and forms of expression, these being phantasy, eating, and defecation, all three functions considerably distorted in the obsessive compulsive neurotic.

This is of course an over-simplification of both views and does not take into account such factors as anal seduction, phallic anxiety, and regression, cloacal phantasies, etc.

Essentially the question is, comparing Freud and Sullivan: can the defecation pattern, consequent to a thwarting of anal libido, affect ego structure; or, as Sullivan would suggest, do the interpersonal issues between parent and child result in security operations which use excretory activities for expression?

The problem is neatly paraphrased by the dream of a young woman who as a child suffered all the usual experiences which destined her later obsessive, compulsive neuroses: she is grappling with an older woman who in the course of the struggle inserts a finger into the patient's anus and extracts a mass of feces. Here we see clearly both the interpersonal and the libidinal struggle. Clinically we must deal with both and work through attitudes of disgust, guilt, anal erotism and dreams, anal seductive longings and compulsive anal obstinacy. This mountainous superstructure ordinarily must be dealt with before we get to the child's basic anguish and doubt, "*What did Mother think of me?*"

Whether the need for security makes for diffidence to authoritative parents with consequent sexual repression; or whether the threat to sexual function makes for security operations and their expression through traits or symptoms—the therapist must consider both probabilities, and respect the facts of both. The libido theory remains to my thinking a useful operational concept even though from a genetic standpoint, Dr. Sullivan correctly emphasized the more basic problem.

His position is underscored by the remarks our patients sometimes make when they refer to the gains from the analytic experience: "I feel as if I have found my self-esteem," or "I am better able to accept myself—and others," or "I find that it is really possible to trust another person." Their reference is almost always to their "self" and not their erotic function. Nevertheless, as an indicator of therapeutic progress their orgastic potency remains a useful criterion.

We find something of the same situation when we consider differences in technique which both Drs. Thompson and White pointed out was devised for compulsive and schizoid disorders. Let us compare an hour with Sullivan and an hour with a Freudian analyst. Again I will oversimplify and credit both with a degree of rigidity which we see in neither.

The Freudian analyst recedes behind the patient into anonymous and amorphous obscurity, out of which the patient models his transference imagery; he lies on the couch in the illusion of helplessness and dependency, and anything at all that comes to mind is invited: phantasy, dreams, events, transference attitudes, and infantilisms. The direction of the work is regressive toward the infantile, toward a setting aside of adult, stereotyped constraint. Freud works from the current dilemma back to the infantile neurosis.

With Sullivan the work is egressive. Sullivan more immediately seeks a way out of the dilemma. He places himself very much within awareness, does not encourage dependency, or transference acting out, or infantilisms. He wants facts, events, and reactions. He accepts the ancient historical data but believes that in any current context one can find the same attitudes and affects; he distrusts "free association" as a meandering in obscurities; he suspects infantile indulgence—the neurotic is infantile enough without encouragement.

The Freudian would encourage the patient to look at his unfulfilled instinctual needs, his origin of self-judgment concerning these, and the consequences to his ego. Sullivan would insist with different emphasis: look at your experience with people; look at the problems, barriers, and disappointments arising between yourself and others, and how they have limited fulfilment.

A total evaluation might be summarized as follows: Freud's formulation of hysteria and therapeutic management has not been improved on, to the extent that the patient is hysteric and not schizoid; and Sullivan has given us our most advanced insight into, and techniques for dealing with, schizoid personalities —to the extent that the patient is schizoid and not hysteric; and we must realize that we see, and must usually deal with in any individual case, hysterical, obsessional, and narcissistic defenses. Sullivan's recommendations as to technique have broad application both from a research and practical standpoint, in the many modifications of psychoanalytic technique which are now being tried: so-called "psychoanalytic psychiatry," short-term therapy, and the progressive efforts of the internist to explore psychosomatic complaints without becoming involved in a transference neurosis.

There are many such differences each contrasting with the Freudian viewpoint; each may well add insight to the other, and possibly not detract from the validity and usefulness of the other. Let us consider briefly from such a perspective certain conceptual differences as regards the process of recovery. The Freudian seeks to make the unconscious conscious, and thus extend the domain of the ego. Sullivan would suggest that an increase in the domain of the ego does not necessarily follow the freedom to indulge in the infantile and that the therapist after acquaintance with the patient's infantilisms was justified in a wide range of manipulations or pressure to effect a choice.

Freud would suggest that after awareness is gained, it is then up to the patient to endure the phobic anxiety and that the positive transference, insight, and encouragement would help.

Sullivan would suggest that the therapist could not rest in making the patient *aware* but that he was obligated as well to assist—by pressure, direction, and education—in making possible the transition from neurotic infantilism to more constructive satisfactions and social purposefulness in living. In this sense Sullivan was more Meyerian than Freudian.

Freud would feel that improvement would follow a divestment from the infantile of libidinal cathexis. A libidinal maturation would follow spontaneously. Sullivan would accept the need for such abreaction, but saw the dynamics of improvement as consequent to the possibility of a choice, if the patient could learn of the alternatives and why he has not seen an alternative.

His concept of the "self-dynamism" suggests a potentiality for health more than the concept of an ego helplessly embedded in the infantile Id, and barricaded behind and by a Super-Ego. Sullivan would suggest that to think of the Ego as hemmed in between circumstance and the instinct-ridden unconscious was a dodge, a rationalism. His respect for the individual's capacities to be something more than a compromise between circumstance and instinct conveyed itself to his patients. With this there was an unpretentiousness and honesty which made it possible for him to say, as Dr. White suggests, things to patients which if attempted by a psychiatrist with any tinge of pomposity would result in either humiliation of the patient or genuine hatred for the therapist. He had a conception of the individual as capable of surmounting almost any circumstance, and considered yielding to circumstance in large measure a ruse for self-indulgence and evasion. He would not accept for himself or for his colleagues the limitations imposed by illness or even those calamities of the final decade. Speaking of an esteemed and loved colleague who had cancer, he exclaimed, "My God, must he then take to his bed and die!" Man's obligation and greatest source of self-contentment was to live out his capacities to their limit, and to extend these to the very last.

Despite his dourness there was an optimism based on conviction that no matter how great the mess there was always a way out, even if the way out was not evident to the therapist. He urged his students never to let a patient go with the final conviction within them that things were helpless and nothing could be done. One could not imagine Sullivan saying to a patient, "Well, we have had a trial analysis and psychoanalysis cannot be of use to you. Goodbye."

In evaluating Sullivan's stature and contributions we cannot ignore Sullivan's provoking position among his contemporaries, both as a personality and as a contributor. As a person he was a gadfly among psychoanalysts, a master of Socratic irony. His complete self-honesty, intensity, contempt for smugness, outrage at psychoanalytic rationalizations, incited the most intense loyalties and animosities. His distrust of psychoanalytic clichés or formalized speculation, his insistence on preciseness of thought, his capacity to transpose the intuitive into the graphic, made him unexcelled as a teacher. He was an inspiration as a civilized human being, if at times a very irritating one. Those who studied under him became students, not disciples, and feel obliged to agree neither with each other or with Sullivan. Sullivan would have it this way: if a student or a patient agreed with a premise or an interpretation, he advised having an alternative one on hand, in response to which if honesty prevailed, some thinking would get done and not just an impasse of amiable intellectual inertia. Those students who became his patients sometimes felt unclear as to whether he had them in the classroom or the consulting room; his impatience with obtuseness could be equally intense in either circumstance. His drive to teach was unarrested to the last, and its effect on psychiatric developments will not be fully felt until many more sessions of review such as that which has been arranged for us on this occasion.

SULLIVAN AND THE
SOCIAL SCIENCES

CHAPTER V

SULLIVAN AND FIELD THEORY

GARDNER MURPHY and ELIZABETH CATTELL

College of the City of New York

I

TWENTY years ago, when he was already a veteran in the study of schizophrenia, Sullivan wrote: "It was thus possible to facilitate the tendency of personalities to enter into group relationships, and to form syntheses of attendants and patients which were most valuable in promoting recovery of the patients. Once freed from the inconsequentiality of ordinary ward service, suitable personnel could gain rapidly in appreciating the significance of interpersonal interplay. The mental hospital became a school for personality growth . . ." [1]

Such passages, still imperfectly understood by those who think of a therapist as one who removes a mental disorder from a patient as Androcles removed the thorn from the lion's paw, show that field theory, as embodied in Sullivan, was neither an academic hobby nor a verbose reformulation of Freud, but a recognition of the true interdependence of all men. We might say that in Sullivan's practice the disorder is not only an aspect of a personality whole, but an aspect of a complex social situation

[1] Sullivan, H. S., "Socio-psychiatric Research," *American Journal of Psychiatry*, 1931. 10.

expressing the interactions of numerous individuals and of a cultural matrix beyond.

Or we might approach Sullivan's position historically by saying that when clinical psychiatry appeared as an entity, in the hands of Emil Kraepelin, the disease was inside the patient, just as an ulcer or a tumor was inside him; that with Freud the phenomena of transference began to make embarrassingly clear that two persons were involved in every symptom and in every step toward cure, the analyst serving as temporary surrogate for the persons who were or are the psychosocial reality of the patient; and that with Sullivan the conception of a disease inside the person, carried around by him intact from one situation to another, was frankly abandoned, with a clear recognition that all we really see and deal with is a career line of interactions between individuals; and that if this be so, it is the relationships, not the individuals, that become our concern.

To some this may appear to be a perverse concern with abstractions. Much the same has been said about Kurt Lewin's [2] rather similar conception of the field in which we live, to which he gave the name "life-space," and of Moreno's [3] situational approach with its definition of the interpersonal totality known as the "social atom." Why does it not do just as well to study each person as an entity, in the manner of the biographer, and then simply put the parts together like a jigsaw puzzle? To answer this question clearly, one may do two things. First, one may look at the history of a comparable development within the physical sciences, leading to the development of the theory of fields not as less real but as more real than fixed particles; second, one may look at the evolution of those aspects of psychology and psychiatry in which the classical conception of persons and their interrelations were found to be unsatisfactory.

Classical physics, as Einstein and Infeld [4] have reminded us,

[2] Lewin, K., *A Dynamic Theory of Personality*, New York, McGraw-Hill, Inc., 1935.

[3] Moreno, J. L., *Who Shall Survive*, Washington, D. C., Nervous and Mental Disease Publishing Co., 1934.

[4] Einstein, A. and Infeld, L., *The Evolution of Physics*, New York, Simon and Schuster, 1938.

consisted largely of pushes and pulls. If a particle happened to
be pulling on another particle, that was so to speak just a question of the external relations, the foreign policy, of the two
particles; it did not bear upon their internal affairs. The study
of electromagnetism during the nineteenth century gradually
showed the inadequacy of this conception. The interactions between events give definition and form to the events; the event
is an aspect of a context, a field, not definable in terms of its
inner essence. This newer conception invaded biology in the
experimental embryology of Spemann and Weiss, who showed
that the growing embryo is not an assemblage of particles, but
a mass governed in its growth by a definite field structure, with
organizing poles and the dependence of any given cell upon its
location and the forces acting upon it. When an immature cell
is grafted into the eye region of an embryo, it becomes eye tissue. When grafted in the ear region, it becomes ear tissue.[5] The
body is not made up of independent cells which somehow work
together; the cells become expressions of their environing fields.
In psychology it became evident to Kurt Lewin that the indivis-
ible reality of our experience is a structured whole, with place-
direction trend; in short, psychological movement within life
space. Dynamically, the character of this space is determined by
the field forces operating within it. In the social sciences it was
becoming clear that the individual is so deeply immersed in the
culture which has reared him that it is no longer meaningful to
define society as a group of individuals who (as an afterthought)
happen to be related in a particular pattern; the individual is a
compelling and vivid node in a field of social forces which he
expresses and through which his individuality is realized.

In the 'twenties it became likewise clear, partly through the
influence of the social sciences, partly through increasing sophistication of psychiatrists, not only that patients, when in the consulting rooms of different psychiatrists, may say different things,
smile, yawn or cry in different rhythms, and call to their assistance various mechanisms of defense, but that their whole conception of themselves and of society may vary with the personal-

[5] Weiss, *Principles of Development*, New York, Henry Holt and Co.,
1939.

ity of the therapist; in every practical meaning of the term, they may become different personalities. Not only, however, was it realized that the psychiatrist's personality was important; it became more and more clear that the world from which the patient came and to which he returned after the visit to the psychiatrist was the only context to which his personality, even his "inner inner" personality could be anchored. Diagnosis must be diagnosis *in situ*, or *in vivo*—not the specification of a disease, but the specification of a disturbed relationship. Therapy becomes not only the imparting of a new outlook in the office, but may involve the reconstruction of the patient's entire milieu.

In Sullivan's own words, "When we speak of impulse to such and such action, of tendency to such and such behavior, of striving towards such and such goal, or use any of these words which sound as if you, a unit, have these things in you and as if they can be studied by and for themselves, we are talking according to the structure of our language and the habits of common speech, about something which is observedly manifested as action in a situation. The situation is not any old thing, it is you and someone else integrated in a particular fashion which can be converted in the alembic of speech into a statement that 'A is striving towards so and so from B.' As soon as I say this, you realize that B is a very highly significant element in the situation . . . The situation is . . . the valid object of study, or rather, that which we can observe; namely, the action which indicates the situation and the character of its integration." [6] It is for this reason that we find Sullivan remarking: "We can improve our techniques for participant observation in an interpersonal situation in which we are integrated with our subject-person. This is evidently THE procedure of psychiatry. I urge it as implying the root-premise of psychiatric methodology." [7] The therapist, says Sullivan, is the "alleged expert whose expertness is to show itself, if at all, in uncovering the processes at work in the patient's relations with others." [8]

[6] Sullivan, H. S., *Conceptions of Modern Psychiatry*, p. 24, Washington, D. C., The William Alanson White Psychiatric Foundation, 1947.

[7] Sullivan, H. S., *Conceptions of Modern Psychiatry*, p. 5.

[8] Sullivan, H. S., *Conceptions of Modern Psychiatry*, p. 46.

Sullivan evidently thought long and hard about field theory in the physical sciences, and about the similarities and differences between these physical fields and the fields of interpersonal relations, as the following quotation reveals:

"People behave in interpersonal fields. The patterns of their performance reveal the field forces by virtue of the people's susceptibility to these forces; but, unlike the iron filings, these people who in their behaving reveal the interpersonal fields are to an extraordinary extent the result of their past experiences with interpersonal fields. It does not make a great deal of difference so far as today's 'behavior' is concerned whether a particular particle of iron has always or only very occasionally been subjected to a strong magnetic field. The time sequence of historic exposure to interpersonal fields may greatly affect the 'traits' which a particular person can be said to manifest in a new interpersonal field. Past experience in interpersonal fields, and the time pattern of such experiences, may greatly affect one's susceptibility . . . in the fields in which one participates . . . The first step towards this science has seemed to be the observation and analysis of behavior in interpersonal fields . . .

"The people in, and in a sense constituting an interpersonal field are more or less aware of the tensions and energy transformations which occur. They have all the primary data there is. If you are one of them and if you are skillful enough, you may be able to observe the progress of events, tensions, and energy transformations well enough to have something to analyze, and on which to base inference. As your skill increases, you will be able to validate inferences, your provisional hypothesis about events, by influencing the interpersonal field." [9]

The forces that guided Sullivan to this way of thinking were of course both outside and inside himself; and they implied both keen perception of what was happening to his patients and also a personal identification with them. From his descriptions of cases one feels he deeply loved those people who embodied his subject-matter—difficulties in living intuitively—and stood against any trend in psychiatric theory or practice that might turn out to be not in line with the hope and expediting of their recovery.

[9] Sullivan, H. S., "The Study of Psychiatry," *Psychiatry*, 1947, 10.

One never feels he is attached to a dogma, but always to service to the distressed. One finds tenderness and sympathy, the capacity to vibrate in unison with the patient who at the time is being described. It is small wonder that the gift of empathic response is so heavily emphasized by Sullivan, or that sound mental health is conceived so clearly in terms of the capacity to put oneself in the place of another and see through another's eyes. Thus of the period of preadolescence he says: "One now begins to learn because knowledge is demonstrating its usefulness to oneself and one's friend." [10] Here, perhaps, we find Sullivan abstracting from his own development; real learning was what he shared in new experience with his friend. Indeed, this elemental core of the process of interpersonal living is at the same time Sullivan's own personal gift as a psychiatrist and his conceptual frame of reference for the theory of sound living. His field theory is no higher-order abstraction from the data of the social sciences, but his formulation of what he actually did as a healer of sick minds.

All this is equally evident in his delineation of the primary roots of mental disease. These roots lie not within the tissue system of the individual, as in the classical conceptions of pathology; they lie in a transpersonal reality requiring that we study at the same time the person and his life situation. It is not the one or the other that is sick; it is the form of the interaction. Psychiatry cannot be carried out adequately within the four walls of the consulting room; at best, the consulting room is simply a sample of a series of life situations upon which it may therefore shed some light; at worst, it is a poor sample, and needs to be supplemented by what one sees happening in hospital ward, or office, or playground, or shop, or family. The diagnosis must be an empathic response to empathic phenomena. And if this is true of diagnosis, it is even more strikingly true of therapy. Therapy likewise often goes on only falteringly and imperfectly in the doctor's office; it may be spread out, for instance to inculcate favorable attitudes towards the patient in those who are of particular significance to him. And, of course, the patient is never a passive object being manipulated, but himself is groping

[10] Sullivan, H. S., *Conceptions of Modern Psychiatry*, p. 21.

towards an understanding and control of his social participation. The result is the "expanding of the self to such final effect that the patient as known to himself is much the same person as the patient behaving with others." [11] It follows inevitably that other people beside the patient are treated therapeutically; indeed, as the patient learns from the psychiatrist, the psychiatrist learns from the patient. This calls for humility and irony; and Sullivan had both.

There is a close parallel here both to the conception of sociatry as developed by Moreno and to the conception of group dynamics as developed by the followers of Kurt Lewin. We are not in the least interested in allocating priorities and assigning credits; nor are we disposed to deny that there are also gross differences between these three systems. But we are intrigued with Moreno's conception that just as life is a stage, so the stage may be used to let the patient act out his life part, in the company of his wife, his family, his friends, his doctor, with some members of the group taking the part of "alter egos," supporting the impoverished ego of the patient, and throwing as it were into relief the "intra-psychic" tensions which this interpersonal situation entails. Not only does the psycho-drama permit "projection" of the patient's attitudes upon the other members of the little drama; it may directly reveal the interpersonal world which the patient does not know how to reveal in words alone, even to himself or even to his doctor in the consulting room. Here is a conception closely and constructively allied to Sullivan's conception of the rebuilding of the patient's world as a first step in interpersonal therapy. Similarly, we are intrigued by the development, under the general conception of "group dynamics" of the conception of personality reconstruction, for example, the transformation of an authoritarian into a democratic leader, as a result of "group atmospheres" or "social climates." The three movements, and several others which belong to contemporary applied psychology, are expressive of the broad conception of social cultural factors in every manifestation of personality, and therefore necessarily of every effort towards education or therapy.

[11] Sullivan, H. S., *Conceptions of Modern Psychiatry*, p. 117.

II

What then specifically is the pathology that disturbs our everyday capacity for empathy, for constructive integrations with others? It is behavior engendered originally by demands too severe to be met, and by disapproval too poignant to be tolerated. The child comes to attend to only that in his performances with others which is not too unbearably painful; to ignore the anxiety-fraught aspects of his behavior that seem to promise overwhelming failure or rejection. And this split between what is within awareness and what is outside of awareness largely determines the nature of the person's relations with others. What is within awareness becomes the "I"; but what is ignored is not destroyed. Hence follows the array of dissociated or parataxic behaviors, still purposeful, but fulfilling those interpersonal tendencies which cannot be accepted by the primary centers of activity and awareness, the "I," the "self" who acts wittingly.

How does this self arise through social interaction? How does the social world confer a self on a child? According to Sullivan, "The self-dynamism is built up out of . . . experience of approbation and disapproval, of reward and punishment . . . as it grows it functions . . . right from the start. As it develops, it becomes more and more related to a microscope in its function . . . It permits a minute focus on those performances . . . which are the cause of approbation and disapprobation, but, very like a microscope, it interferes with noticing the rest of the world . . . when anything spectacular happens that is not welcome to the self . . . anxiety appears . . . In other words, it is self-perpetuating . . ." [12] These socially conferred dimensions of the self are of utmost importance to mental health or illness. When limitations and peculiarities of the self interfere with the pursuit of biologically necessary satisfactions, or with security, the person is mentally ill. Some of the mentally ill achieve a self with the emotional tone of "good," continually endangered by the intrusion into awareness of portions of the personality not in keeping with this generally quite unbiological goodness; while others

[12] Sullivan, H. S., *Conceptions of Modern Psychiatry*, pp. 9-10.

acquire a hateful self—"bad" on the irrational basis, perhaps, of being girls instead of boys, or resembling one side of the family rather than the other—and with them human warmth and friend- liness are dissociated.

This building up of a constricting self-system does not occur under the influence of parents alone, but of teachers and signifi- cant others throughout the course of a lifetime. One notices the departure from Freudian thinking in that the origin of neurosis or psychosis lies neither in a specific episode in the past nor in a specific person who imposed unbearable burdens upon the grow- ing child, but rather in a trend as broad and pervasive as the culture to which we belong. We are soon led to a general pattern prevalent in our commercial-puritan culture which demands the impossible by way of achievement and at the same time disap- proves the naive biological demands which might give the self some day-by-day fulfillment and therewith some sense of belong- ing, some sense of adequacy to life. And while one finds in Freud the Platonic conception of the magnificent isolation of the self— "Where Id was, there shall ego be"—one finds in Sullivan the following: "You will have grasped the fact that we . . . sub- scribe to the dictim of 'know thyself' in the very particular sense of 'Learn to recognize the interpersonal fields in which you find yourself, and how to influence the field forces in the direction of more certain definition of the fields and their more adequate and appropriate integration.' " [13]

Growth for the patient means his coming to try out in suitable situations motivational systems that have been dissociated. He must learn precisely what his parataxic behaviors are as the first step towards far-reaching change. He discovers, often by learning to attend to dreams, subtle changes in tension, marginal thoughts, unwitting acts, and sequences of all these rudimentary evidences of impulses in complete opposition to the way he sees himself, or the role he tries to play with others. He comes to recognize that the pressure of overpowering circumstances once led him to renounce resources that now in significantly different situations he can afford to cultivate; that the security operations complicat- ing his relations with others were once natural adaptations, the

[13] Sullivan, H. S., "The Study of Psychiatry," *Psychiatry*, 1947, 10.

best he could do in the face of difficulty, but that only his failure to differentiate the present from past keep them appearing as required. In field-theory terms, since the self is always a self-in-situations-with-others, changes in the way self and others are experienced occur in unison. As the patient expands his awareness of himself, he concomitantly achieves a richer, more real awareness of others.

And just as the patient's disorders developed in unfortunate interpersonal situations, his growth likewise usually depends on a special facilitating situation. In becoming aware of what goes on in his relationships with others the patient is guided by the hypotheses of the psychiatrist. But Sullivan pointed out that his considering, and therefore potentially benefiting from these hypotheses, may depend on the presence of mutual sympathy, either on conscious or unconscious grounds; and also on the continuity of the relationship, which results from the psychiatrist's having a deliberate purpose of entering constructively into the life of the patient. The patient comes to recognize the psychiatrist's striking difference from those who originally contributed to his constricted self-system. He finds himself in a situation in which hitherto dissociated impulses may be given the benefit of elaboration in consciousness, synthesis with the rest of the personality, foresight, and modification based on recognition of the presence of others. And as the patient begins to relate more appropriately to the psychiatrist, he learns to relate more appropriately to others.

Growth is generally dependent on a series of insights into specific, concrete situations. For instance, the spontaneous elementary discovery by a ward patient that the inmates and attendants were not malicious but only stupid might be a turning point towards some initial adjustment. The female patient who learned that when a certain anxiety arose she started accusing the doctors of bringing her to a den of racketeers had gained some insight into how she was complicating her predicament. A series of insights can explain the miscarriage of an intention (or an incongruity between effort and effect) or clear up the whole mystery of a lifetime of self-defeat. The deep enthusiasm that many people have for analysis seems often related to their coming to perceive dynamic structures with considerable temporal extension where before there was chaos. They see the how and the why of experience that troubled them not only as ungratifying but as mysterious. And yet of course the complex structures revealed—for instance, harsh childhood producing a harsh self, operating so as to perpetuate harshness in the present environment, with dissociated tenderness intervening so as to keep the solution of harshness from ever seeming quite satisfactory, however glorified—are not for the purpose of explanation, but for reconstruction. One understands so that what is obsolete and maladaptive can be discarded.

And these specific insights lead not only toward cure for those with particular difficulties in living, but towards insight into the difficulties of the living in the broadest sense. Sullivan believed in the fully social origin of knowledge, that "information can arise only from explicit or implicit attempts toward communication with other persons . . ."[14] Thus the analytic situation in which the patient is stimulated to communicate and hence formulate what he believes is going on in his relations with others, and in which his version can be checked against that of the psychiatrist and both versions against direct experience, may be said to be the matrix not only of cure for the patient but of psychiatry as a science. We learn that many or most people maintain false pictures of themselves adapted to their false pictures of others which are in some way related to the people they experienced in childhood; and we learn the role of such falsifications in the situations in which they occur, and also their relation to the underlying reality that they violate. We learn that people develop elaborate value systems to assert the opposite of what they fear they are, what they repudiate in themselves not on any realistic basis but only because of the distorted demands made on them particularly in childhood. Thus we see that the most elaborate value system may serve the humblest and most self-interested function. In the social sciences, too, Sullivan points out "the investigator participates more or less unwittingly in the data which

[14] Sullivan, H. S., "A Note on the Implications of Psychiatry, the Study of Inter-Personal Relations, for Investigations in the Social Sciences," *American Journal of Sociology*, 1937, 42.

he is assembling," [15] and under certain circumstances, "Discovery
. . . bears a most intimate relationship to the habitual unwitting
preoccupations of the investigator; tends to remedy his insecurities, so to speak, rather than to illuminate social reality." [16] It
seems evident that our ideals, our values, and our intellectual
methods may all profit by psychiatric elucidation.

One might expect that considering the distress and unbearable tensions that most of those with mental disorder suffer, the
exploration of a new self in a new universe would be enticing to
the patient; but this is not the case. After all, all the satisfactions
he has known, and all those he has envisioned, have occurred
within the confines of the familiar self, however rigid. He is faced
with giving up whatever satisfactions he has known for others
he knows not of, or whether he will ever achieve. Also, in order
to change he must undergo the immediate discomfort of attending to those areas of living which are highly charged with anxiety; he must make tentative use of dangerous motivations formerly excruciatingly punished; and further he must lose the
feeling of the familiar to risk the unknown, all of which must
arouse anxiety. And, as Sullivan says, anxiety is the one thing
on earth no one wants. Thus while patients need to change, as
their patterns of living with others are inadequate, they are also
highly motivated—by the threat of anxiety—to remain as they are.
The tendency of life to move in the forward direction must push
against a strong inclination to conserve the status quo however
unsatisfactory.

Making anyone aware of aspects of reality about which he is
highly motivated to remain uninformed is perhaps the most difficult task of education. Therefore it is interesting to see what
philosophical assumptions Sullivan regards as useful in the performance of this service. First, there must be the assumption that
"we are all more human than otherwise," eliminating any basis
for contempt or guilt, or any negativistic supposition that collaboration is by the nature of things impossible. Second, there is the
assumption that "since social situations are reciprocal they can

15 Ibid.
16 Ibid.

be transformative," putting up to both parties in an interpersonal situation, or at least to the better qualified, the responsibility of transforming it in a constructive direction. Third, there must be the recognition that the reality which may be said to underlie our very real misconceptions is safer to live with than the often glorious and plausible misconstructions we have erected for our short-term comfort. Fourth, destructiveness, whether involving verbal attack or merely indifference to another's anxiety or often influential misapprehensions, never fits the exigencies of a mutual field. Fifth, there is ultimately no need to pander to any special needs or handicaps that are not a matter of organ deficiency or immaturity, each member of an interpersonal integration having the right to respond to the uncompromised requirements of collaboration.

III

Now as to a brief critique of Sullivan's approach. We would raise three questions: (1) Did Sullivan explain in field terms the specific origins of specific kinds of maladjustments? (2) Did he show that field theory can cope with present realities without our getting lost in the attempt at reconstruction of the past? (3) Did he escape the bias of a special acculturation in regard to the implication of field theory for the cultural reality which lies behind both psychiatrist and patient?

(1) If all of us are subjected to the imposition of the burden of a limiting self, and of parataxic escapes from full social participation, an exact explanation is needed for the fact that one of us develops a psychosis, another a neurosis, while a third passes for normal. It is quite understandable that psychiatrists dealing with sick patients have been more concerned with factors contributing to the cure of mental illness, than with a precise definition of factors involved in its genesis, which would for the most part lie outside of their control. However, Sullivan specifies that "just as a locality deficient in iodine may be related to endemic goiter—a specific deviation of development—so the surpluses and deficits in the personal environment of the growing person determine peculiarities and deviations of personality de-

velopment." [17] Yet, we find in Sullivan's *Conceptions of Modern Psychiatry* no clear indication of the primordial factors—or sequence of factors—which start the trend in one direction or another, explaining for example why the *psychopathic* type of personality develops in one case, the *incorrigible* in another. Each may have gone through early experiences producing a negative self, but this is a long way from specifying the interpersonal situations—or series of situations, acting on a progressively modified organism—that give rise to specific syndromes.

This lack of explicitness regarding the origins of the various kinds of maladjustment is not a matter of accident in a well-rounded system. The fact is that none of the field theories of today give a concrete account of the specific factors which precipitate a specific type of functional failure. Even when the individual is well along with his growth, we lack the knowledge to predict with finesse the transactions which will occur when he confronts a specific opportunity, or a specific threat.

It may be asked whether any kind of psychology is better off in the matter of prediction. Yes, those kinds of psychology which are close to physics, as, for example, those relating to simple sensory responsiveness or simple motor expressiveness, can utilize the field knowledge which physics has already developed; the organism end, so to speak, of the transaction, involves the physics and chemistry of tissue, and the quantitative laws that emerge, as in the relation between stimulus brilliance and capacity for visual discrimination, are simply the laws of physics revealed in a special case. But the laws of the whole man, in response to the whole situation, are not at all likely to emerge from the study of these part-properties of sensory and motor elements; they are much more likely to emerge from the laws already taking shape in such fields as ecology and economics—and psychiatry—in which complex interpersonal realities are evident; but they will of course take into account far more dimensions than any existing discipline can describe.

(2) The second difficulty in the use of field theory in psychiatry is the question when to use past transactions in defining the present field. Strictly speaking, the past as such is not prop-

[17] Ibid.

erly used in any formulation of field events; the past has, so to speak, its surrogate, its aftermath, in the present; we cannot mix past events as such in the field forces which are the determination of each individual's conduct. Sullivan was aware of the problem and termed it, "the most difficult element in the field theory of interpersonal relations." [18] That Lewin likewise was worried about the matter is evident in many of his writings, and nowhere more than in his determination to follow physics in dealing only with the present, a determination which resulted in his calling psychology an "ahistorical" science—a science which eschews history. Sullivan, as we saw, finds a place for the past in loading the operation of forces in the present—in perduring motor sets, in learning that "leads readily to error," in the "eidetic people" which are "potent representations of persons one has encountered" which one carries around with one. This means, whether we like it or not, that the individual has inside him remnants—or "reminiscences," as Freud says—and that these remnants interact with new situations and make trouble. But this idea of the individual's carrying within him fragments from previous situations is exactly what we thought we had gotten away from. Would it not be best to admit candidly that in this respect field theory has failed to clarify the fact that it is only the present—rich as it is in heirlooms from the past—*only* the teeming present that counts?

Indeed, the event which we recall from the past and which blends with the present to activate us is not quite the event as it occurred in the past's context—for, like Heraclitus, we never cross the river twice; yesterday it was a different river, and we who crossed it were different men and women from the men and women who will cross it today. As Sullivan said of the "eidetic people" they do "change, however slowly; they, too, are altered by experience subsequent to the occasion on which their particular prototype exerted effect on one." [19] However, if this is true, does it not behoove us to know how the present selects and transforms a past event, how a present event shapes what it

[18] Sullivan, H. S., "Multidisciplined Coordination of Interpersonal Data," *Culture and Personality,* p. 189, edited by Sargent, S. S. and Smith, M. W., New York, Viking Fund, Inc., 1949.

[19] Ibid.

evokes? Yet if at times his presentation lacks clarity in this re-spect, still in the tough practical task of teaching us to think in terms of Heraclitus, Sullivan, despite occasional lapses, did as much to bring us face to face with the field realities as any man of this present era; while at the same time making us aware of the vicissitudes undergone by such realities when screened by a motivational system so warped that equilibration from a state of anxiety takes precedent over the attainment of satisfac-tion and security.

(3) Our third difficulty is Sullivan's relative neglect of the forces emanating from the over-all structure of our society—a neglect rather surprising from the field theory approach. In con-sidering the influences of these forces, perhaps one of the diffi-culties is that a statement relevant to one social group is apt to sound strikingly parochial in respect to other groups. For in-stance, Sullivan states that fear is rather rare in the civilized world. But for whom is it rare? And where? Mrs. Lindbergh in China before the last war described the discrepancy between how a famine was experienced by a group of upper-class Ameri-cans waiting for a plane to take them home and by the Chinese peasants who would remain among the dying. Does not the psy-chiatrist with an interpersonal view also need a world view?

Sullivan says that within our American culture we are all judged more or less according to "whether we get our just deserts because we know how to go after them." He derides the attitude towards the mentally ill on the part of the general public and attendants and even some psychiatrists and the mentally ill them-selves (as part of their difficulties), that they are "failures, hope-less, despised, damned." But this attitude towards those not demonstrating their fitness, which is by no means confined to the mentally ill but spreads to the aged, those on relief, and most non-prospering groups, would seem to us largely a reflection of our highly competitive system. Psychiatry holds up collaboration as a mature form of interrelatedness—a step upward from coop-eration—but is collaboration really given an adequate institu-tional basis by our social structure? What happens to the mem-bers of a society who are taught that they must get their just deserts because they know how to go after them, though periodically it is impossible for a large percentage to get their deserts at all? At a time as from 1930 until the war, when there were ten million or so unemployed, could psychiatric treatment of individuals have solved the problem?

The community tends to approve institutions that ameliorate the sense of insecurity, such as religion and national baseball, while it taboos the use of its institutions for the open-minded study of many of the very problems from which insecurity arises. Sullivan refers to "the most insecure culture I know—the American culture" and says that ". . . for a great majority of our people, preadolescence is the nearest they come to untroubled human life . . . from there on the stresses of life distort them to inferior caricatures of what they might have been." [20] Certainly one of the stresses that cannot be written off is the stress of economic insecurity, and of a Right-Left dichotomy and the lack of unbiased investigations and thinking in this area. Sullivan deplores the attempt to find a solution "on the far side of chaos." But one wonders if there is not some scotoma involved, some selective inattention since no solution on the *near* side of chaos is suggested. The attitude towards radical change as something fearful, with the emotional tone of "far side of chaos," is curious in a psychiatrist who dealt with getting patients to face chaos in tearing down their existing modes of operating in order to establish better modes, even though, as Sullivan describes the process, "Not only is there this element of great change, but also there is no possibility of foresight as to the direction and extent of the change. Finally one could not foretell that this change will be tolerable; there is every prospect of its including serious conflict, for the self-dynamism includes powerful tendency systems which are responsible for the character of the present life course." [21] Yet against such inertia the psychiatrist must oppose the requirements of growth. Sullivan presents the radical as motivated principally by destructiveness, as someone who "shows no durable grasp of his own reality or that of others, and his actions are controlled by the most immediate opportunism." [22] Yet Sullivan's

[20] Sullivan, H. S., *Conceptions of Modern Psychiatry*, p. 27.

[21] Sullivan, H. S., *Conceptions of Modern Psychiatry*, p. 70.

[22] Sullivan, H. S., *Conceptions of Modern Psychiatry*, p. 96.

description of a group life that distorts the majority into inferior caricatures of what they might have been seems at least to leave room for the possibility that radicalism may have some other basis besides personal maladjustment. Perhaps in some cases at least the courage to challenge a frustrating society is an expression of strength rather than weakness. However, Sullivan does not of course reject the struggle towards a better society, and in a sense his attitude towards a sick society is as optimistic as his attitude towards the mentally sick. He states, "The general outline of the useful task of the psychiatrist and the social scientist would seem to be the amassing of valid information about living, and the changing velocity of social forces would seem to give increasing opportunity to accomplish this." [23] And "it is probable that the adaptive capacities of man are greatly in excess of the demands of current life, and it is clear that consensually valid information is useful in meeting the contingencies of existence." [24]

IV

We believe that Sullivan's system of ideas contains within itself the guarantee of a steadily broadening vision which will in time rectify all such shortcomings as the three we have seemed to find. For it always seeks the concrete reality of the patient's whole interpersonal world.

The psychiatrist must, for example, know throughout the course of the analysis what his place may be in the patient's system of values; what place the patient has in his, the psychiatrist's own system of values; what kinds of conscious and unconscious transactions are likely to go on during therapy and beyond therapy; he must take cognizance of what the place of the doctor-patient relationship in our culture may do to his integration with a particular patient. The doctor-patient integration in which the psychiatrist is a kind of senior partner in a team of participant observers would seem likely to discourage either the infantilism

[23] Sullivan, H. S., "A Note on the Implications of Psychiatry, the Study of Inter-Personal Relations, for Investigations in the Social Sciences," *American Journal of Sociology*, 1937, 42.

[24] Idem.

on the one side which Fromm has reminded us is likely to result from the situation in which the psychiatrist may put the patient; or the authoritarianism on the other which Sullivan reminds us may arise as a function of what may be required by the patient or his family or by the cultural definition of the respective roles. But the therapist knows that he can do little without the collaboration of the patient, that his expertness comes largely through his having been in the patient's place in an analytic situation, even that some firsthand experience of considerable mental illness may improve his capacity for empathy, and that his valuable imperturbability itself is largely a matter of the carefully arranged limitations of the doctor-patient relationship. However, the psychiatrist is not belittled by the recognition of these facts: he is probably the first person in our society who has by the very nature of his job come to realize that it is not he who does something to or for another person; he is an aspect in a complex transaction which both expresses and changes him.

It would be utterly fatuous to debate here as to the degree to which orthodox Freudian analysts, with their emphasis upon counter-transference and upon their own unconscious warping of the therapy, have come to similar conclusions, or as to whether the trend represented by Sullivan is a fulfillment, or a negation, or a plagiarism, or a revolution. Sullivan saw the reality, and put it into practice with energy and devotion. In so monumental a restatement of human relations there is credit enough to go around, and to make us grateful that so many people, each with his own insight, came in this period to grasp more fully the degree of our interdependence upon one another.

CHAPTER VI

SULLIVAN'S CONTRIBUTION TO SOCIAL PSYCHOLOGY

LEONARD S. COTTRELL
Russell Sage Foundation

NELSON N. FOOTE
University of Chicago

HARRY STACK SULLIVAN has a secure place in history as the man who defined psychiatry as the study of interpersonal relations. Many of us regard social psychology as the study of interpersonal relations. In attempting to assess Sullivan's contributions to social psychology, since he virtually identified it thus with psychiatry, we are almost in the position of having to report all that Sullivan ever did or thought or wrote. We shall have to be highly selective, therefore, in order to suit the space available, and shall undoubtedly display our bias in what we choose for appraisal.

Harry Sullivan was not simply an intermediary who brought two disciplines, or the members of two disciplines, together. His magnificent talents as a matchmaker produced many more marriages of minds than that. He was responsible for hundreds of introductions across the boundaries of craft and clique—anthropologists, physiologists, government officials, academicians, hospital administrators, students, patients, publishers, writers. Had he never written a word, founded a journal, delivered a lecture, or helped to organize an institution or an association, the abundance of his cosmopolitan friendliness would nonetheless have been an important force in knitting alliances between psychiatrists and all those others who cope professionally with problems of living in present-day society. The range of faces whom we have recognized here tonight testifies that his exuberant curiosity about what the other man has to say is still fermenting among us.

Sullivan not only brought about introductions, but strove to create situations in which further mutual acquaintance and co-operation would grow. For all its distinctive character, *Psychiatry*, the journal of which he was primarily the founder, is one of the least sectarian of all scientific periodicals. Through the medium of its pages, the interpenetration of once-segregated disciplines continues. Physicians discover debts to philosophers; political scientists observe anew that disturbances of digestion may cause and be caused by clashes of empire. Ethics, semantics, economics, pediatrics—nothing human is foreign to those strangely colored pages. As recently as the new book on communication by Ruesch and Bateson,[1] a psychiatrist and an anthropologist, we find instances of collaboration, stimulated during Sullivan's editorship, continuing to mature. In whichever of the many afterworlds known to them which they have chosen to inhabit, we can imagine Sullivan eagerly talking shop with Edward Sapir, the great anthropologist and linguist, who was a major architect with Sullivan of the culture-and-personality rapprochement. During the past year we have learned of a number of instances of the addition of social scientists to the staffs of medical schools and hospitals, a development of which Sullivan was a pioneering champion. When he died, as we all know, he was attending a world conference on mental health which he had helped to plan; his last published article before his death, if we are not mistaken, was his masterful contribution to the UNESCO conference on *Tensions Which Cause Wars*,[2] in which he partici-

[1] Ruesch, Jurgen and Bateson, Gregory, *Communication: the Social Matrix of Psychiatry*, Norton, New York, 1951.

[2] Cantril, Hadley, editor, *Tensions Which Cause Wars*, University of Illinois Press, 1950.

pated with social scientists from half a dozen countries.

Now these reminders of the many channels through which Sullivan made—and is still making—his influence felt, are being elaborated further by other members of this symposium. We note them here to demonstrate two points:

(1) The individuality of Sullivan—if it be not blasphemous to ascribe such to one who regarded the idea of unique individuality as the mother of illusions—arose from the vigorous practice into which he put his doctrine of interpersonal relations; indeed Sullivan and interpersonal relations have become almost synonymous. He was not simply an aspiring intermediary, but was himself a successful synthesis, who demonstrated in action the validity of his views.

(2) The greatest honor we can pay Sullivan—the one that he himself would surely deem most appropriate—is to carry forward the program that he so diligently instituted. That his program retains remarkable momentum despite his absence is evident in every quarter which was quickened by his presence. Nevertheless, if these memorial meetings add some further energy to that program, they will be splendidly justified.

Above all, we must not diminish any of that momentum or slow down in any way the current which he has engendered. This *caveat* is particularly important as we turn now to consider Sullivan's ideas, for it is the ideas of a great man which most readily get frozen into static monuments by those who admire him.

In this respect Sullivan, we can be sure, would apply to himself and to us, his pupils, the same words he applied to Freud: [3]

"The great debt that psychiatry owes to Sigmund Freud does not require us to try to stop our thinking at the points at which his thinking ceased. If anyone thinks that Freud, or any post-Freudian psychiatrist, has reached or approached the Truth; well and good; but that one is not a scientist. All scientific hypotheses must undergo change as man's grasp on the Universe con-

[3] Ibid., p. 87 n.

> tinues to develop. This cannot but be strikingly the case
> in the traditionally neglected fields of psychiatry and
> the social sciences."

For all his effect along the other channels noted, it remains our
conviction that it was above all through his characteristic ideas
that Sullivan contributed to social psychology. They should not
be embalmed but made to live and grow through further research and application. What we essay, therefore, is to select
certain of those conceptions of modern psychiatry which Sullivan evolved during the last fifteen years and to exhibit them as
gateways to the further development of the study of interpersonal relations. This program of ideas, as it were, can be advanced by all those who confirm its importance by their presence
here. It ought to be prosecuted along all those lines on which
Sullivan prosecuted it—in clinical practice, in research among all
the social and psychological disciplines, in teaching, in conferences of theorists and practitioners right up to the international
level. As we envisage such further development, it will appear
that we are speaking of research. Primarily we shall be: that is
our own special interest, and we are eager to promote in thoroughly substantial ways research of such promise. But Sullivan
derived his seminal formulations only partially and vicariously
from research as such; and like him, others will carry forward
what he has commenced only by the full and cooperative utilization of the whole repertoire of the scientific enterprise.

Here then is the program, captioned in terms of major Sullivanian conceptions. Sequentially it is ordered very much like
the three types of performance which he expected from his patients: [4]

1. *Physiological substrates:* For every interpersonal act, there
is a correspondingly physiological *mobilization* (our term) which
can be investigated and identified. This is not the old doctrine of
psychological parallelism, but a contemporary, researchable improvement, so different as to be almost unrecognizably descended

[4] Sullivan, Harry Stack, *Conceptions of Modern Psychiatry*, W. A. White
Foundation, Washington, 1947, pp. 99-100.

from it. Emphasis has shifted from the physiology of perception and sensation by the individual organism to the preparation of the organism to act appropriately toward the conceived interpersonal meaning of the stimulus. Stimuli, moreover, may be "prehended" outside awareness, even be illusory, and yet evoke quite extreme mobilizations—"energy systems," in Sullivan's terminology.

Such a conception implies a very definite stand on the cloudy question of emotions. Emotions, in this view, are the manifestations of abortive mobilizations to act, in ways which the current interpersonal situation, whether for real or imagined reasons, both demands and forbids.

Sullivan says in several places that the phenomenon of "anxiety" as a psychological phenomenon is difficult if not impossible to detect; it often operates outside awareness. But almost without exception, any psychiatric patient—or any person interested in study of himself—can acquire skill in noting shifting physiological conditions—the sudden reduction of skeletal tonus in laughter, the tightening of long muscles in shyness, his peculiar patterns of respiration and perspiration, of heart and stomach action. Furthermore, as these physiological substrates of interpersonal events are conscientiously related to the interpersonal situations of their occurrence, they become pregnant sources of information as to the meaning of some of the more obscure performances of the self-system.

Here is surely an avenue of progress to be explored. We already have in the literature of psychosomatic medicine and medical research a host of evidence as to the array of physiological effects produced by stressful interpersonal situations. We have in mind such items as Lindeman's work on the incidence of colonic ulcers among the bereaved,[5] the really mountainous data on the connection of gastric and cardiac disturbances with severe competition and other fear-provoking circumstances, the correlations of hypertension with suppressed aggression. Too many of these psychosomatic studies, however, limit themselves

[5] Lindeman, Erich, et al., Study in progress at the Laboratory of Social Relations, Harvard University.

unduly to variants of Cannon's famous "emergency reaction." [6] In future psychosomatic research, which is not obliged to be limited to those stress reactions which cause physical breakdown, we need more attention to the incidence of some of the lesser symptoms. We have noted some welcome tendencies to pioneer along these other lines in the experimental work of investigators like Trigant Burrow,[7] Harold G. Wolff [8] and others. Instead of more on hunger, fear, pain and rage, a great deal of light on interpersonal relations would be shed by careful study of the precise physiological and sociological concomitants of those meaningful symptomatic acts, the yawn and the sigh.

If you now engage in a yawn or a sigh, you have the data at hand to commence your investigation immediately.

The same observation may be made with respect to the laugh, a very complex physiological performance of peculiarly human and interpersonal significance. Sullivan only dealt with laughter in passing, unlike Freud, but we know he reflected upon it as a datum to be explored further when he could find time in his crowded career.

Sullivan's delineation of the intricacies of the interview situation is probably the most penetrating in print, and surely the most alert to all that occurs. He not only took careful note of every physiological occurrence he could detect, but sought to sensitize his subject to report others not visible externally. His procedure suggests potential collaboration between clinic and laboratory.[9] We need to bring certain kinds of physiological recording apparatus into the interviewing clinic, where they are normally lacking. Conversely, the clinic has available for testing and systematic experimentation in the laboratory a multitude of practical insights into the interpersonal conditions which can be

[6] Cannon, Walter B., *Bodily Changes in Pain, Hunger, Fear, and Rage*, Appleton, New York, 1920.

[7] Burrow, Trigant, "Emotion and the Social Crisis: A Problem in Physiology" in Reymert, Ed., *Feelings and Emotions*, McGraw-Hill, New York, 1930.

[8] Wolff, Harold G., "Life Situations, Emotions, and Bodily Disease" in Reymert, Ed., op cit.

[9] Sullivan, Harry Stack, *Conceptions of Modern Psychiatry*, p. 35.

artificially set up to bring about certain normally-rare physiological states. For example, much experimental work has been done on patterns of salivation, which needs to be related to our knowledge of oral dynamisms construed in interpersonal terms.

On the level of theory, we are badly in need of a systematic classification, not of the legion of psychosomatic symptoms, but of the modes of interpretation of psychosomatic symptoms, or as some would say, a theory of symptom choice. Just as Sullivan sought to develop a typology of disordered interpersonal relations as a substitute for classification of disorders by Kraepelinian symptomatology, we need to be able to distinguish with confidence and in far more detail those behavioral and psychosomatic anomalies which can be identified in such ways as these:

a) foreshortened symbolizations of forbidden acts;
b) paralyses due to conflicting mobilizations;
c) consequences of strain due to over-mobilization;
d) "power operations," like stammering and headaches;
e) disruptions of function due to acute attention to an organ.

These are only suggestive, but may be sufficient to indicate the promise for research in physiology inherent in the interpersonal view.

The general formula for such exploring and theorizing must be that which distinguishes the specific physiological substrates of specific classes of interpersonal acts, incipient and overt. No one more scrupulously avoided than did Sullivan the fallacy of reductionism, in which social and psychological phenomena are treated as merely physiological events; yet no one more fully appreciated the extent to which every physiological event was instrumental to and indicative of social significance, and therefore highly germane to the study of interpersonal relations. If we continue along the route he has sketched, we are certain to realize much.

2. *Motivation as a grammatical illusion:* Very closely related to the idea of mobilization which we have just outlined is Sullivan's incomplete but revolutionary conception of motivation as a situational phenomenon. By this we mean not his shorthand

usage of the terms *satisfaction* and *security,* but his relatively lengthy (for him) discussion [10] of motivation as a summation of integrating tendencies called out by a situation. Although he spoke of the seeking for satisfaction and security as the "two great motors" of human behavior, elsewhere he made plain that these were simply names for two broad classes into which it was convenient for certain purposes to divide human behavior. He never displayed willingness to reify these categories and use the reifications as explanatory first causes. On the contrary, he deplored and apologized for the shortcomings of traditional language, which encourages reversion to faculty-psychology.[11] He no more upheld the old notion of motives as entities within an individual than he upheld the idea of personality traits as individual possessions. We can fully endorse his position, which remarkably parallels that of several thinkers in quite different fields.[12][13]

The implications of this conception of motivation are almost unexplored. We find the socialized human organism prepared to respond in any one of several ways to each consecutive situation it encounters. As a congeries of stimuli, only mutually consistent by rare good fortune, the situation usually sets off more than one impulse to act. Until these are unified in a single, though perhaps quite complex, definition or program, action is suspended, or at least severely impeded, since the organism normally can only act *overtly* as a unit. The resolution of these multiple incipient lines of action is problematic; optimal resolution by no means regularly occurs. The problem of motivation, therefore, is primarily one of organization and harmonization; it is not so much that of explaining the "force behind" each of the incipient courses of action which activate their specific mobilizations in the organism. The organism is always acting; it has at hand all the capacities, powers and energies to make actual any

[10] Ibid., pp. 95-98.

[11] Ibid., p. 24.

[12] Burke, Kenneth, *A Grammar of Motives,* Prentice-Hall, New York, 1945. See also his *A Rhetoric of Motives,* Prentice-Hall, New York, 1950.

[13] Lundberg, George A., *Foundations of Sociology,* Macmillan, New York, 1939.

of the potentialities which cognition finds relevant (even if mistakenly) to the situation confronted. The degree to which that situation can be defined in a unified manner is the degree to which capacity and energy are released for performance of the appropriate act. The degree to which the situation is variously defined, giving rise to counter-impulses which tend to enfeeble or even to paralyze each other, is the measure of conflict, frustration and apathy. As Sullivan emphasized with the eloquence at his command, this conception of motivation leaves no place for such occult entities as will-power, superego, psychic energy or death instinct. It is at once matter-of-factly interpersonal and matter-of-factly physiological. To the extent that he mentions such familiar notions as tensions and drives, these fall under the heading either of specific organic *irritations* (our term), which constitute problems for the person, or of specific organic *mobilizations*, which are readinesses to perform sequences of action intended to resolve problematic situations. It would have been pushing the interpersonal conception too far to have asserted that all motivation arises solely externally to the organism, in its relation with others. That is why it is necessary to grant that a large class of actions have to do with the relief of organic irritations. On the other hand, these organic problems can be solved in a more or less wide variety of ways, depending upon the person's previous experience and the values of his community of significant others, e.g., favored diet, so that, while the irritation is specifically given, the mobilization to remove it is not. Irritation and mobilization are not identical in fact, and should not be merged conceptually, especially when the mobilization is instrumental to a specifically symbolic end-in-view, like winning a game.

By thus quite clearly exorcising all quasi-biological entities as the causes of motivation, Sullivan has opened the door to a remarkable array of freshly-phrased problems for social psychology. For example, we can visualize many fresh lines of attack on the quandaries of people whose low motivation arouses complaint by themselves or by others. In particular, we have here the suggestion of an incisive strategy for dealing with the fatigue and hypochondriacal syndromes, in their societal as well as their individual manifestations.

If we take into account that all of us—whether laymen or professional—must make use at least implicitly of a theory of motivation whenever we seek to induce another to act, we can foresee great gains to be made in our own competence in interpersonal relations by transforming our presuppositions about motivation into consensually-validated information. We can only mention here this important window which Sullivan has cut into our ignorance, not detail the vistas which lie beyond it.

3. *The self-system and its significant others:* As you know, the main stream of American social psychology has been a continuous evolution and elaboration of the concept of the social self. This development stretches back unbrokenly at least as far as Emerson. In the hands of those who tried to give it scientific treatment, it can be traced through such important names as James, Baldwin, Cooley, Dewey, Mead and Thomas, plus dozens of lesser contributors. Sullivan is beyond question the most important recent member in this series. His contributions to the basic formulations of George Herbert Mead are substantial and vital. We would not consider a course in social psychology complete which did not include Sullivan's elaborations of the social self.

Parenthetically, we have wondered frequently how someone who had so completely mastered the social psychology of the self as Sullivan could show so few signs of having perused the actual literature of this stream of thought. Did he pick the ideas up through his training with Adolph Meyer and his wide-ranging conversations, as an alternative to reading? Or do we have here a true case of independent discovery and invention, with resulting clinical confirmation of the findings of people like Mead? Whatever the answer, our function here is to point out precisely what his important additions and modifications were, since these seem thoroughly original and timely.

The correspondence between Mead and Sullivan leaves off at the point of the generalized other. For Mead, whose life-span came a generation before Sullivan's, the social world was a fairly wholesome web; the others from whom one took his conception of himself were in substantial agreement. Hence, the "generalized other" of Mead's social psychology. In Sullivan's time, and ours, the community has been fractured. The generalized other has broken down into clusters of significant others, and the validation of right conduct is more problematic than ever. Sullivan himself describes well the change: [14]

> "In the Western culture, into the second decade of this century, there was no devastating divergence of the religious rules from the main trends of the culture-complex. With the short-lived emergence of the Communist idealism and the still-spreading reversion to Totalitarianism as a doctrine of the state, the practical solidarity of the Western culture was destroyed. There are now many significant differences in the culture-patterns which are impressed on children in home and school, and through the channels of mediate acculturation. A great deal that was unquestionable has now become controversial, if not obsolete. Whereas once one 'belonged' or was an outcast, the question now is rather *where* one belongs than *does* one. Each party, group, and clique has its own normative rules, its own orthodox attitude to the religious and even the legal systems. The differences in these respects between the most extreme groups are greater than any differences of belief that have previously influenced the peoples of the world. The ideologies (dogmata) that find devout believers even among our own people are strange indeed to survivors of a time when one's 'conscience' could be one's guide."

Under these conditions, personal identity itself becomes problematical for many people, because one can, and often does, participate in several groups of significant others; if these groups are not in accord, the conceptions of self which accrue to the person from his diverse involvements can only be in discord. The organization of conduct which will engender a sense of security and self-esteem when performed becomes thus far more difficult, breakdown far more imminent in critical situations. It is acute realization of these dilemmas of the mobile cosmopolitan of today which constitute Sullivan's most important modification

[14] Sullivan, Harry Stack, *Conceptions of Modern Psychiatry*, pp. 95-96.

of contemporary theories of the social self. Premised on this analysis were constructed his exceedingly valuable elaborations of the conception of *consensual validation,* his partially successful efforts to translate *substitutive processes* into interpersonal terms, and his definition of the goal of psychiatry as the expansion of the self through bringing as much as possible of what is inattended or dissociated into the realm of consensually-validated information of the self. Also, we no doubt should emphasize his conception of the self as a postulated center of emerging kinds of interpersonal behavior, only partially characterizable or systematized by verbal conceptions, rather than as a metaphysical entity somewhere within a person. In thus presenting the self as a social product—a set of reflected appraisals—he was less original, but his treatment is more precise at many points, than Mead.

Certainly this line of development is not dying out. We are gratified to note the vigor with which Dr. Norman Cameron of Wisconsin, another Meyer student and an avowed follower of Mead, is pushing his development of such closely similar conceptions as *public verification* and *pseudo-community.*[15] Already since Sullivan's death a number of items by other writers have appeared which carry forward the study of problems of identity, on which he verged and in which he would have been intensely interested.[16]

There is much more to be done than has been done. Not only will supplementary increments be made to our knowledge of self-other relations, but some of Sullivan's earlier ideas on these will have to undergo clarification and correction. We remain confused, for example, by his attempt to explain just how a derogatory conception of the self resists change in the face of attempts by others to correct it. We definitely doubt his assumption of the permanence of early patterns of personality development—not that such permanence does occur, but that it *necessarily* occurs, and that the exceptions are as few as he seemed to suppose.

[15] Cameron, Norman, *Psychology of the Behavior Disorders,* Houghton Mifflin, New York, 1947.

[16] Foote, Nelson N., "Identification as the Basis for a Theory of Motivation," *American Sociological Review,* 16, 1, 1951, pp. 14-22.

Indeed, we should go further, since we claim some license for speculation here, to assert that when the whole Sullivanian conception of the effect of significant others upon the origin and stability of self-conceptions is pushed further, really revolutionary vistas of guided personality change emerge. If the maintenance of certain characteristic patterns of interpersonal behavior depends upon their support by significant others, then to alter the composition of any person's community of significant others is the most direct and drastic way of altering his "personality." This can be done. Indeed, it is being done, with impressive results, by the many types of therapeutic groups, or quasi-families of significant new others, which have come up in the past few years. It is a matter of regret that his many duties and preoccupations prevented Sullivan from taking a more active part in the development of what we broadly term group therapy. Many group therapists are building their new developments on very shaky theoretical foundations, or on no theoretical foundation at all, proceeding by rather haphazard trial and error. Had he lived Sullivan would surely have moved into group therapy quite thoroughly by now and we firmly believe would have contributed heavily to the theoretical basis which the field requires. Indeed it is not too much to claim that even now his writings offer the best theoretical foundation for group therapy as yet in print. To be sure, something still better is due. In particular, we are just now in great need of careful study and theoretical formulation of the process of involvement and identification. Just how do significant others become significant? And just how do formerly significant others become insignificant? Having our eyes upon the physical dependence of the infant, we have quite neatly and thoroughly begged these questions in the past, perhaps by implicitly assuming that the psychological significance of another could be reduced to mere physical dependence, a moment's reflection upon which is sufficient to reveal its fallacy, e.g., identification with peers. In a community which is fractured like our own, the practical problem of bringing about constant reidentification of persons with groups who can validate their behavior is no less pressing than the theoretical problem.

Thus we can thank Sullivan again for placing his contribution to the social psychology of the self squarely within the context of contemporary problems of living.

4. *Parataxic integrations:* Freud declared that psychoanalysis stands or falls on its doctrine of the unconscious. Unfortunately this has too often been taken to mean that his particular formulation of unconscious motivation could not be improved upon. If we had to choose the conception of modern psychiatry which has been the most valuable of Sullivan's contributions to social psychology, it could well be *parataxis*, because with it Sullivan has taken "the unconscious" out of the realm of uncontrolled imputation and made it researchable. It is a major improvement upon Freud's concepts of unconscious motivation and of neurotic behavior, and it is fundamental.

What Sullivan has done is to translate the large, loose notion of unconscious motivation into more dynamic, interpersonal, situational terms, a metamorphosis carried out with exquisite precision in the first main article he wrote for *Psychiatry*. Parataxic integrations are incipient interpersonal acts. They are always evoked in a specific situation involving other people, in which they compete for the resources of the organism with the more appropriate, consensually-validated acts which become overt, and thereby complicate the latter in varying degrees. Instead of construing these parataxic integrations as obscure forces operating in some topographical nether-world of the individual psyche, they are brought out into the light of potential recognition as interpersonal acts of the same qualities and forms as the more valid acts to which they relate as uncongenial alternatives.

The observation that alternative definitions of the situation, not unified within a master definition, may persist as tendencies to action, in differing degrees of awareness from conscious conflict of loyalties through selective inattention to full dissociation, is also a refinement of Freud's basic concept of repression in interpersonal and more researchable terms. In conceiving of the self-system as the custodian of awareness, finally, Sullivan has refined the gross character of Freud's Super-Ego and made it easier to delineate with exactness those specific self-other integrations which provoke particular restrictions of attention.

As a corollary to his psychological analysis, Sullivan can take a more hopeful philosophical position on the possibility of achieving rationality. In elaborating his conception of rationality in terms of consensual validation by significant others of the appropriateness of acts, he puts us into a position to designate with progressive clarity just wherein rationality can be said to inhere, and how to cultivate it.

It would be well if we could go into some detail regarding the systematic interconnections of these basic concepts. Our purpose tonight, however, we must reiterate, is to treat them as gateways to further development of our knowledge. We see great importance in our getting firm observational and conceptual hold of the varieties of these parataxic integrations, and the conditions of their occurrence. We want to recognize, identify, and name them, perhaps eventually work out some kind of classifications. With such a grasp, interpretations of their origins and prescriptions for their modification may acquire a higher probability of correctness. Instead of hunting around in the depths of the psyche, our general strategy of procedure must be to explore these various parataxic definitions of the other ("transferences" in Freud's terminology) which could evoke the kinds of reactions observable. This becomes a matter of contemplating relevant social roles as hypotheses, the range of which is normally limited in the experience of any individual. That is, one asks what roles, corresponding to what competing definitions of the interpersonal situation, are struggling for expression.[17] Once the identity which an observed person is imputing to another is

[17] Sullivan was hampered in developing a general formulation of the dynamics of interpersonal situations and particularly of parataxic processes by his failure to grasp the significance and utility of the concept of the role. For a discussion of this concept as a tool for the analysis of interpersonal situations, see three articles by Leonard S. Cottrell, Jr., (1) "Roles and Marital Adjustment," *Proceedings of the American Sociological Society*, vol. 27, 1933, pp. 107, 115; (2) "The Case Study Method and Prediction," *Sociometry*, vol. 4, 1941, pp. 358, 370; (3) "The Analysis of Situational Fields in Social Psychology," *American Sociological Review*, vol. 7, 1942, pp. 370, 382.

discerned, the most bizarre behavior becomes comprehensible. Using Cameron's cognate terminology, we can affirm that, if the pseudo-community to which the psychotic is responding were as real to others as to himself, his behavior would seem perfectly reasonable and conventional. In his sensitive analysis of the psychiatric interview situation, Sullivan always strove to find out what identity or identities the patient was imputing to the psychiatrist, as being the most important determinant of what behavior he would disclose. Utilizing Sullivan's conception of parataxic integrations, some of the ostensible irrationalities of race relations become much more explicable. At Cornell University it has already been found that the concept of parataxis together with the concept of role greatly increases our understanding of racial attitudes and the conditions of their eventual control. Dr. John Dean, the field director of the research on intergroup relations, feels confident already that we can set up situations experimentally so that a hotel manager, for example, will or will not discriminate against a Negro guest, as desired.

Frankly, we do not see why the concept of parataxis and indeed the whole interpersonal vocabulary have not already swept the field. It would be one of the ironies which Freud himself might enjoy if the concept of the unconscious, which had to make its way against all sorts of unreasoning resistance, should in turn oppose equal inertia to its own improvement.

5. *Empathy:* By what means is the clinician or other scientific observer to recognize the signs of parataxic integrations when they occur? Is he to rely entirely upon training his subject to report physiological changes, marginal thoughts and would-be suppressed thoughts? And how are the reports of the subject to be validated and interpreted? Here we find Sullivan reviving the older concept of *empathy* and commencing to give it an operational statement as the non-verbal communication of emotional states.

Verbal and non-verbal communication are never separated in actual behavior, save perhaps in written communication, and even in print parochial idioms convey far more meaning than is ever grasped by the foreign reader. By separating verbal and non-verbal analytically, however, and seeking to sensitize himself and his subject to all kinds and nuances of non-verbal communication, Sullivan has opened an important gateway to expansion of our knowledge of this vital aspect of interpersonal processes. In his theory of development, empathy performs a crucial function in what goes on between infant and mother before the acquisition of language and commencement of the childhood stage. It seems certain that many more emotions and attitudes are conveyed by empathy than just anxiety and taboos; also, it is likely that empathy not only lingers on, but actually increases in versatility and precision after the acquisition of language, rather than diminishing, as Sullivan supposed, even though it merges with many complex processes of inference as experience lengthens. Possibly the peculiar deadness of schizophrenic communication [18]—its absence of non-verbal elements, alongside its linguistic creativity, in which Sullivan took such sympathetic interest—influenced him to underemphasize the functions of empathy among normal adults. At any rate, here is a field for further investigation, to which Sullivan has given invaluable impetus. While he did not succeed in producing the operational statement of empathy which he set as his ideal goal, he has at least helped to rescue the concept and its referents from the limbo of mysticism to which undiscriminating earlier critics had consigned it, and to set it upon the way to full scientific status. Since we have dealt at some length with potential research on empathy on other occasions, including an article in *Psychiatry*,[19] we shall prophesy no further here as to where this impetus will take us.

6. *The mediation of human experience by language:* While non-verbal communication plays such an important part in Sullivan's formulations, his emphasis upon verbal communication was even more prominent. He loved words and their power, and played with them creatively to our lasting debt. We do not refer

[18] In his book, *The Biology of Schizophrenia*, Roy G. Hoskins suggests that schizophrenia may be the result of a lack in empathic capacity.

[19] See Leonard S. Cottrell, Jr., and Rosalind F. Dymond, "The Empathic Responses," *Psychiatry*, 12, 4, 1949, pp. 355-359.

to his literary talent, however. Other psychiatric theorists have dealt with myth, symbol and rite, but Sullivan is unique in his concern with the interpersonal functions of language *per se*. Perhaps he picked this up in part from Adolph Meyer. Also, he was certainly influenced by the positivist trend and by his friendship with Sapir. In the main, however, it is his own original contribution, and a weighty one, the significance of which has only begun to be explored. At some points in his writings, certain of Sullivan's insights into the uses of language seem to have been arrived at through the intuition of sheer genius, they are so directly apprehended. In re-reading him to pick out his analysis of language functions, it has been remarkable how every page of his is permeated with realization that language is the *sine qua non* of interpersonal relations, from his description of the cry as the magic tool of the infant through accounts of distortions of communication in behavior disorder to his definition of psychiatric cure as "the expanding of the self to such final effect that the patient as known to himself is much the same person as the patient behaving with others." Before Sullivan, it would have seemed fanciful to require a student of psychiatry to take a course in semiotic, the theory of signs; since Sullivan, it seems almost obligatory. It is not practical, however, to summarize here all the fresh insights he has garnered through his heightened consciousness of this peculiarly human medium. Instead we can only call attention to three of his theoretical elaborations of the interpersonal functions of language: in consensual validation, in information, and in the intricate reciprocities of the interview situation. These in turn can be summarized as a general phenomenon which is one of the most important gateways Sullivan has opened to further pursuit of knowledge.

In essence, what we have to deal with is this: the regularities in human behavior are not innate but learned. In order to organize our behavior toward the world, and particularly toward other persons, we must categorize all things. To categorize is to name and to name is to know in the sense of knowing how to act with respect to the object or situation categorized. Moreover we must categorize as others categorize; society is only possible through shared meanings.[20] We speak to each other in words, every one of which is a general concept. If we are to communicate and interact successfully with each other, our ascriptions of meaning must be in accord. To the extent that they are not, we experience frustrated expectations and consequent difficulties in living. These can only be cleared up by validating our meanings against those in more general usage. But such validation, especially with respect to verbal definitions of ourselves, is best facilitated when we can talk without fear with intimates of similar experience, as in conversation among preadolescent chums. Lucky are those who retain such perfect intimacy thenceforth, because they are few; hindrances to truth of intercourse multiply rather than diminish. Communication thereafter falls especially short of accurate representation when the person is struggling to arrive at an appraisal of himself which will provide satisfaction and security. His self is virtually synonymous with the appraisals which he has heard from others, and these may be diverse, derogatory, hostile. If he is to develop a self-system which will give him a sufficient degree of competence for coping with his interpersonal environment, he must know as far as possible what others expect of him, must know who he is and what he is capable of, what the effects of his actions are in the appraisal of himself by these others. "Let us repeat, in this connection," Sullivan says,

"the statement that one has information only to the extent to which one has tended to communicate one's experience—through the medium of consensually valid verbal means. Theoretically, this last qualification gives somewhat undue importance to the use of words; by and large, it is a good principle to which to adhere in

[20] The classic statement of this conception of language was, of course, made by G. H. Mead in his lectures on *Mind, Self and Society*, University of Chicago Press, 1934. Sullivan either borrowed the conception or developed it independently. In either case, he put it to the test in clinical applications and enriched it by discovering empirically not only its general validity but in pointing out the many ways in which the process of communication and consensus are complicated and obstructed. See especially Harry Stack Sullivan, "The Illusion of Personal Individuality," *Psychiatry,* 13, 3, 1950, pp. 317-332.

treatment work. Most patients have for years been acting out conflicts, substitutions, and compromises; the
benefits of treatment come in large part from their
learning to notice what they are doing, and this is greatly
expedited by carefully validated verbal statements as to
what seems to be going on." [21]

To obtain such information, to have it in place of illusions and
in spite of parataxic elisions, one needs to talk freely and fully
with a significant but uncensorious other. Psychiatric cure does
not commence to progress until patient and therapist have
achieved that relationship in which they can collaborate in consensual validation, particularly of the patient's ideas about himself (but not exclusively, since the therapist too undergoes expansion or complication of his self-system, depending upon the
success or failure of the interviewing process).

What Sullivan has uncovered in this hastily-sketched analysis
of the attainment of interpersonal information is entry into one of
the most fascinating research areas that is going to absorb attention and resources, we think, during the next few decades. In a
sentence, it is the discovery that *by investigating social psychological phenomena, we change those phenomena,* and by involving the subject or subjects in participation with us in the process
of investigation, these effects are powerfully enhanced. We doubt
if this discovery can be attributed to Sullivan, or for that matter
to any other individual, since it has been repeatedly noted by
various writers in the social and psychological sciences during
the past several decades. Hitherto, however, these reflexive effects of investigation upon the investigated—called by Robin
Williams [22] the Heisenberg indeterminacy principle of the social
sciences—have been regarded primarily as nuisances by scientists
holding to the older contemplative or spectator philosophy of
knowledge. Only very recently has it begun to be grasped that
these effects can be studied and exploited constructively as a
generalized method both for scientific research and for producing desired changes in persons and groups. Sullivan deserves

[21] Sullivan, Harry Stack, *Conceptions of Modern Psychiatry,* p. 110.
[22] Williams, Robin M., In personal communications.

some of the credit for the development of this method to date, and certainly for the impetus to push its development further. He called it *participant observation*, endowing that traditional phrase with fresh meaning. Rather than pour new wine into old bottles, we have preferred to rename it *participant experimentation*, since it implies more activity and purpose than is connoted by mere observation, and also it definitely involves experimentation.

For further discussion of this departure in methodology, and its application, we must refer you to a forthcoming publication under our joint authorship.[23] From our experience to date, we can testify that Sullivan's imaginative insights, into the way the naming of conceptions of self by persons or groups confirms or alters their previous identity and subsequent behavior, have contributed more to social psychology than even he probably knew.

7. *American values:* Confronted as they have been by the menace of several totalitarianisms, Americans have been re-examining their conceptions of themselves as a people and a nation. Americans have continually examined themselves in biography and history, but this latest re-examination has been going deeply, systematically and objectively into the very fundamentals of American values and identity. We cannot afford to be wrong about ourselves, in a world such as the one described on Page One of our daily newspapers. In a multitude of ways, obvious and subtle, this spirit of self-searching and self-presentation has infused itself into all the social sciences. It may fairly be said that the relatively passive pseudo-detached orientation represented in the types of positivism and functionalism which flourished during the period between the two World Wars has been giving way to a more active joining of the scientific spirit with concern with the purposive and value aspects of human social life. Sullivan exemplified this new orientation with a clarity and explicitness which few equalled. Offhand, we do not call to mind any social scientist more acutely aware of the crises of values in American society, though no doubt people like Erich Fromm and David Riesman equal his appreciation; and the influence of

[23] A Research Planning Memorandum on The Family, in preparation for the Social Science Research Council.

his leadership along these lines may already be making itself visible in some of the literature of psychiatry which has appeared since his death, e.g., Erikson's study of *Childhood and Society*.[24]

Probably the American value which Sullivan most conspicuously embodied was optimism, his belief in the possibility of progress through the application of effort, imagination and good will. This was no fatuous pollyanna attitude. Ever and again he deplored "our prevailingly juvenile era," spoke of the increasing incoherence of our social organization, and even felt constrained to excuse his dour outlook on grounds that he encountered a disproportionate share of society's behavioral cripples. "Our psychiatry," he says in his *Conceptions*,[25]

> "emerged here in the peculiar setting of our national life; has developed along lines of promise for reciprocal service in the evolution of ever-increasing human dignity, fraternity, and opportunity. It had looked forward with growing confidence to the time when the incidence of grave maladjustments of living would be greatly reduced by virtue of our increasing civilization. A crisis in world-events now imperils all this, and one may well wonder if the emergence of our psychiatry was not much too late in the era of realizing democratic ideals."

His optimism was akin to courage in the face of difficulties, a sort of positive corollary to Franklin D. Roosevelt's famous declaration in the pit of the depression that "the only thing we have to fear is fear itself." That is, Sullivan implicitly recognized that hope in human affairs is one of the most important conditions of the realization of its own object. In his penetrating analyses of how anxiety is basically overcome by giving up self-defeating security operations, this insight is made explicit for interpersonal relations. In operation it produces a reflexive effect of the greatest value in achieving autonomy. Sullivan's collaboration with a patient or a colleague was always a participant experiment in realiz-

---

[24] Erikson, Erik H., *Childhood and Society*, Norton, New York, 1950.

[25] Sullivan, Harry Stack, op. cit., p. 87.

ing those ideals which America took over from the Enlightenment and has further elaborated. "Thirty years of work," he declared near the end of his career.

> "have taught me that, whenever one could be aided to foresee the reasonable probability of a better future, everyone will show a sufficient tendency to collaborate in the achievement of more adequate and appropriate ways of living." [26]

We all recall his aphorism that "the basic direction of the organism is forward." He stated as a preconception his confidence that "personality tends towards the state that we call health or interpersonal adjustive success, handicaps by way of acculturation notwithstanding." This is a belief of the kind that cannot be validated except by acting upon it, hesitation by way of cynicism notwithstanding. Sullivan acted upon it, and verified it again and again.

In so doing Sullivan was being very American. In this respect at least, one can doubt very much the gain to be derived from assimilating him with the sequence of Freud and the Freudians, as Mullahy [27] has attempted in his recent book. Though the spirit of optimism came originally from Europe, it seems to have become America's role to relight its lamps over there. Sullivan's leadership in creating world organization for mental health is a role which others will do him honor in fulfilling.

Another American value which stands out in Sullivan is the admiration of competence, which is very closely related to his belief in the energetic pursuit of progress. In fact, he had gone quite far in substituting *competence* for *adjustment* as the end-in-view of his very broad conception of psychiatry. "The purpose of psychiatry," Sullivan declared, "is the study of living to the end that it may be facilitated." Mental health is defined as competence in interpersonal relations, quite a dynamic conception in

[26] Idem. *Tensions Which Cause Wars.*

[27] Mullahy, Patrick, *Oedipus—Myth and Complex,* Hermitage Press, New York, 1948.

contrast to the *status quo* connotations of adjustment. In the forthcoming work we have already mentioned, we attempt an operational definition of competence, and suggest a series of researches on the conditions of its propagation. In this attempt we make substantial use of Sullivan's contributions.

That brings us quite logically to a third American value which Sullivan quite distinctively embodied, the last we have space to discuss, his pragmatism. Just as he shared the social psychology of John Dewey and George Herbert Mead, he shared their experimental and instrumental philosophies almost thought for thought.

Of Sullivan's pragmatic touch, one illustration only, a striking one. He was much interested in that perplexing transposition of social roles generally known as homosexuality. It is one of the developmental syndromes which he sought to typify in interpersonal rather than symptomatic terminology.[28] This is a subject which has called out a voluminous discussion in psychiatric literature, capped by the conclusion on the part of many that the problem is practically insoluble. Yet Sullivan's approach is so simple and direct as to appear almost perfunctory:

> "Of the treatment problems connected with handling patients of the homosexual developmental type, few require any special consideration. These people may be sufficiently evolved towards adulthood to enter readily into the therapeutic collaboration, in which case the physician's major problem is that of keeping the long-term goal always in sight. This goal must be the dissolving of the patient's barrier to full intimacy with persons of the other sex. The prevalent error is an effort to treat 'homosexuality' as a problem in itself . . ."[29]

That is all. No excursion into bizarre speculations on the causation of the dramatic manifestations. Just a matter-of-fact getting down to business in helping to solve the patient's difficulties in living, yet a solution fundamental in every sense, philosophical,

[28] Sullivan, Harry Stack, *Conceptions of Modern Psychiatry*, p. 104.
[29] Ibid., p. 104.

medical or otherwise. Such level-headed piercing to the heart of the problem—the interpersonal problems of the people involved—is perhaps one explanation for the brevity of Sullivan's writing, on this and all else. When you can hit a nail on the head in a sentence, what more is there to say?

We hope we have done a tenth as well. If we have succeeded in demonstrating that each of his ideas beckons us onward to further quests into the unknown, we can properly conclude—since only yesterday was Columbus Day—by pointing out that Sullivan magnificently exemplifies the original American value, the spirit of exploration and discovery which has characterized us from the beginning.

There are other important contributions, in addition to the seven we have chosen to note, which should be included in any complete list. For example, there is the highly suggestive beginning which Sullivan made in linking certain syndromes with the interpersonal problems characteristic of certain stages of development of the person. Another instance would be his undertaking to translate the substitutive mechanisms into terms of interpersonal dynamics. But enough has been said to make clear why we have for many years held Harry Stack Sullivan to be one of the half dozen truly great figures in American social psychology. We could not propose a more fitting and durable memorial to him than the new horizons of research to which he has oriented us through his conceptions of modern psychiatry.

CHAPTER VII

THE CONTRIBUTIONS OF HARRY STACK SULLIVAN TO SOCIOLOGY

CHARLES S. JOHNSON
Fisk University

THERE is, necessarily, some risk in appraising the broad influence of a single individual on a social discipline. In the very nature of the situation, the risk can be both of an underestimate because more subtle values are unperceived, and of an overestimate because a highly conspicuous and identifiable contribution can carry unwarranted assumptions regarding other elements in the same context.

Further, in attempting to point up significant contributions to sociology, there will inevitably be extensions across the rather vague borders of social psychology and other sub-disciplines within the social science field.

As a psychiatrist, Dr. Sullivan made perhaps the first effective challenge of the biological preoccupation and limited language and concepts of psychiatry for dealing with issues so obviously involved in and a part of the social process. He was undoubtedly the most forthright psychiatrist in recognizing the need of psychiatry for the data of the social sciences, and for collaboration with social scientists in understanding those interactions of persons that are integrated into a dynamic complexity involving traditions, customs, inventions and institutions. He was solely responsible for the formulation of the interpersonal relations theory, which recognizes the inescapable interaction of the individual and the social order, and which recognizes that personality, as such, is manifest in interpersonal situations only.

It was his view that the data of psychiatry are perceived interpersonal events, and that it is from the application of scientific method to these data that the theory of modern psychiatry itself is to be evolved.

We may credit him with the fruitful attempts, even without achieving a final dogma, to formulate a total conception of the interpersonal field, which would include the data and events of the social universe, and with the projection of this conception into new dimensions of human living, about which both the psychiatrists and the social scientists have been vague and inconclusive to the point of mysticism, or downright fatalism.

A first postulate of his conception of psychiatry is that the human organism is made up not only of parts of the psychochemical world, but also of accessions acquired from the universe of culture. Along with the elaboration of psychochemical factors, there is also the progressive elaboration and differentiation of motives. The useful concept contributed by Sullivan to sociology in this context is that of the life process of human personality, the inter-lapping stages of growth, and the acculturation of the growing biological organism.

"Man, the animal," says Sullivan, "expands into or grows to be a person by living through his plastic years in an environment of other people—from which environment he has obtained or comes to include a great deal of the universe to which we ordinarily refer as culture."

The elaboration of our social structure and the changing velocity of the social process made for an increasing number of what he calls "culture surrogates." These are almost wholly the data of sociology: the mother, family group, teachers, companions, chums, friends, love objects, employers, colleagues. It is difficult, if not impossible, for the social scientist to make sense of these relationships without reference to the concept of social role-taking, to which he contributed such illuminating insights. The concept of "social role" describes the capacity of the person to make fluid shifts in form, in varying measure, in accordance with the adaptational requirements of the person's position in society. This is, in essence, the process of social adaptation. Under pressure, the individual may react to the social pressure with compliance, protest or withdrawal. He may, it appears, react to the same pressures in a manner which explains some of the phenomena of war neuroses and psychosomatic disorders. In such a situation the organism responds by disintegrating its old form and structuring a new form with distinct properties of its own.

The insights that can best be contributed to the social scientist by the trained psychiatrist are those drawn primarily from his experience with mental patients. "The peculiarities shown by mental patients," Sullivan has pointed out, "are chiefly overaccentuated or unduly prolonged instances of relatively universal behavior." [1]

Psychiatry has been a specialization of medicine, and medicine as a science has been a biological science. Even though the practice of medicine may be regarded as a particular specialized field of interpersonal relations, the languages of biology and the biological orientation of medicine were regarded by him as inadequate to the needs of psychiatry. Any attempt to make sense of interpersonal events in strictly biological terms, he thought, was doomed to confusion and failure. Sociology and, in particular, social psychology, even though not naturally developed, were concerned with the interaction of the social order and the individual. Since personality phenomena are the data of the psychiatrist and are conditional on the relevant personal situation, it is obvious, he felt, that psychiatry is essentially closer to the social sciences than to biology as such. The need that he stressed, therefore, was for a synthesis that would hold on to much of what is good in the biology of higher organisms, and along with this, much of what is good in the social psychology of the human young, in cultural anthropology and in linguistics, epistemology, ecology, social geography, political science and administration, and for generalizing these data and evolving a

[1] "Psychiatric Aspects of Morale," Harry Stack Sullivan, M. D., *American Journal of Sociology*, vol. XLVII, No. 3, p. 278, Nov., 1941.

new orientation in all these fields of study. In the end it would not be any of these but a general science of human living, and from it a body of specific techniques for living and for the improvement of inadequate living. In the place of the relatively inexplicable failures and successes of our present psychiatric techniques, said Sullivan, there will be precise communicable knowledge.

The Theory of Interpersonal Relations

Lasswell [2] was one of the first of the social scientists to recognize the value of the concept of interpersonal relations. The significant feature for the social science observer, he noted, in the environment of any personality is another personality, and the significant feature in the environment of any culture is another culture. Dr. Ernest Beaglehole in an issue of *Psychiatry* points up the value of Sullivan's theory of interpersonal relations to social scientists and psychiatrists alike. It was elaborated, he speculated, in order to provide a series of insights into the phenomena of human behavior with which the psychiatrist has to deal, but it has vastly wider implications. For it can lead to a more general theory of what human beings are, how their personalities are formed, and how they react to group life. A distinction of some importance is noted, between biological and cultural drives in human behavior. The former seeks satisfaction, the latter seeks security.

The definition of "situation" throws light on the problem of studying individual and group tensions. Redefinition of the nature of "sublimation" and the conception of the growing personality is one which stresses the development of a self-dynamism, a system or dynamism that evolves gradually from the experiences of the child to the experiences of adulthood. These insights into human functioning and into the interrelations of the various social sciences have a profound value for the social sciences themselves. In fact, says Professor Beaglehole, this conception so well formulated by Dr. Sullivan, "presents a general-

[2] "Person, Personality, Group, Culture," Harold D. Lasswell, *Psychiatry*, vol. 3, 1939, p. 533.

ized theory of the individual and his group that seems capable of reorienting many of our conceptualizations of the social sciences." [3]

Contributions to Research Methodology

There are consistent stresses in the lectures and articles of Dr. Sullivan on some of the underlying values of psychiatric method for sociological and social science research particularly with respect to interviewing and evaluation. A considerable consciousness has been aroused in the possibility and dangers of bias and the perverse use of words. He called attention to the overwhelming conviction of authentic selfhood, which usually permeates communicative efforts in research and data gathering in the social science field. As late as 1936 he noted that neither the students of social psychology nor students of social entities and processes were able to evolve any very powerful generalizations for the organization of their data and the formulation of their investigations. [4]

The reason for this, he noted, was the difficulty of being free from serious inhibitions in his awareness as to the stream of events which involve him. The complicating factors inherent in the personality of the investigator are identical with a major preoccupation of the psychiatrist. If the sociologist looks to the individual concerned and not to the processes integrating him with some of these, his data are likely to be incomprehensible. In certain parataxic situations, the alertness of both parties is likely to be seriously inhibited. The underlying reality of the "transference" and "repetitive compulsion" of Freud is a ubiquitous complicating factor in interpersonal relations which cannot safely be ignored in any inquiry into human relations. Verbalizations can obscure as readily as they reveal. To the student of culture, of social environments, of social organization, of social processes

[3] "Notes on the Theory of Interpersonal Relations," Ernest Beaglehole, *Psychiatry*, vol. 3, (1940), pp. 511-526.

[4] "A Note on the Implications of Psychiatry, the Study of Interpersonal Relations, for Investigations in the Social Sciences," Harry Stack Sullivan, *American Journal of Sociology*, vol. 42, p. 848 (1936-37).

or the special aspects of any of these, the psychiatrist can offer some generalization of his experience in dealing with these difficulties of living that are traceable to inadequacies or eccentricities of personality, or even to minor or major mental disorders.

These generalizations would refer to the locus of the social scientist's study, to the evaluation and interpretation of the data, and to the limiting factors that should control his hypotheses. "The crying need," says Sullivan, "is for observers who are growing observant of their observing."

In application of this thesis the Washington School of Psychiatry under him laid plans for the development of techniques for personality study, for psychiatrists and social scientists alike, on a post-doctoral level, designed to use free-associational processes and psychiatric methods on data synthesized from the facts and observations of social scientists.

Roles, and Role Taking in Parataxic Integrations

Sullivan's theory of the parataxic integrations of interpersonal situations has been noted by Beaglehole [5] as opening up an extremely valuable attack on the problems of communication, the function of language, speech and gesture in communicating ideas, emotions, moods, from one person to another, and speculates that further study of these integrations can provide the basis for a new and more powerful study of group life than social scientists now command. Our speech and gestures are likely to be directed towards the other person as defined by integrating tendencies of which we are not aware. The role of the psychiatrist is to discover this "other person." The role of the sociologist is to study the number and varieties of parataxic integrations in order to understand the dynamic character of group life itself.

In general, in the interview situation, the psychiatrist's contribution to the sociologist is that of enough psychiatric sophistication to be aware of likely distortions of communication that will affect seriously the reliability of his data.

The American Race System has engaged the attention of

[5] "Notes on the Theory of Interpersonal Relations," Ernest Beaglehole, *Psychiatry* (1940), vol. 3, p. 518.

many students of intergroup relations. The explorations, or as he called it "psychiatric reconnaissance," into the race system of the Southern states were further evidence of the convictions regarding the relationship of the individual and the group, and of the importance of cultural factors in the definition of personality.

Sociological studies of the Negro in the South suggested the existence of a strong matriarchal dominance in the rural, or plantation, Negro family structure. What Sullivan found was a continuous profound insecurity, a highly significant matriarchal pattern of the family group, two separate systems of vertical invidious classes combined in a system of four castes, a complex, remarkably irrational social organization, a rigid racial etiquette, anxieties, religious beliefs, racial ritual. He directed psychiatrists into this field in association with social scientists with the suggestion that it constituted one of the most significant social science research fields for a beginning study of interpersonal relations. As an incidental comment on the state of the democratic society he referred to this group as "under-privileged strangers."

New Dimensions in Human Living

It is possible that World War II, in which he served as a psychiatric consultant, turned his attention to new problems in the joint province of psychiatry and social science. Some of his most significant contributions to the analysis of group behavior were made in his studies of morale, panic, and solidarity.

The approach to morale is by way of relevant extremes, and begins with the study of demoralized people. Chronic demoralization grades from discouragement to despair. The circumstances in which it occurs are both interpersonal and biological. An acute situation involving need for morale is modern warfare. Some principles of positive and protective strategy against psychological warfare are dissemination of understanding of the social structure in the nation at defensive war, the synthesis of solidarity, the control of disintegrative people, realistic distribution of roles, and the hygienic management of activity.

Finally, I would like to suggest as perhaps the greatest contribution of this student to sociology is the basic philosophy that undergirded his professional insights and direction. Just as one of the most important values from his formulations has been his utilization of positive personal relationships, the most important philosophical contribution is that the purpose of psychiatry itself is that of the understanding of living to the end that it might be facilitated. There was for him a lively possibility and hope that controllable social rather than uncontrollable natural forces were, in the end, the strongest influences in the fashioning of personality. It was this conviction, made urgent by world disorder and the tensions of war, that extended his concern to the spreading virus of racial and religious prejudices, and of international antagonisms. The roots probably lie deep in the fears and illusions that keep men lonely and distrustful in our bewildering modern society.

In an article on "Psychiatry in the Emergency" for the *Journal of Mental Hygiene* in 1941,[6] he made this prophetic observation: "It is obvious that living is essentially dynamic—that there is no static condition in the relations of living things, and their necessary environments. There is this continuous change in the cultural environment of man. Institutions and ideas change. This change is opposed by conservative tendencies which are perhaps derived from our crucial fear of the unknown. Be that as it may, the social organization of any healthy group of people shows progression and the mental health of those who make up the group is functionally dependent on the balance between the velocities of institutional change and human understanding."

[6] Vol. 25, No. 1, Jan., 1941.

DISCUSSION

OTTO KLINEBERG

Columbia University

SINCE I was introduced in the somewhat personal terms of my relationship to Dr. Sullivan, I'd like with your permission to start with an account of some of these personal contacts that I had with him, not only because I hope that to all of his old friends they would be of some interest, but because it seems to me that they do have direct bearing on his relation to social science in general.[1]

Many years ago, a little over twenty years to be exact, when I worked with Professor Edward Sapir, he told me that I must meet Dr. Harry Stack Sullivan. He was the person, in Sapir's mind, who came closest to realizing the value of an integration between the psychological sciences on the one hand, and the science that deals with culture on the other hand, and it was not long after that that I was privileged to sit in on a seminar on "Culture and Personality" held at Yale University under the Chairmanship of Dr. Sapir, and Sullivan was a member of that assembly. It was my first opportunity to see Sullivan in action, and I look back upon those early discussions that Sapir and Sullivan had together, and which they shared with some of their colleagues and students, as perhaps the most important beginning of an interest in this broad area of culture and personality, which as you know, has so influenced the field of anthropology, that sometimes it is a little difficult to decide when a given indi-

[1] The Chairman, in introducing Dr. Klineberg, remarked that the latter had been closely connected with Dr. Sullivan, and that both were together on an assignment in Europe with UNESCO.—The Editor.

vidual is an anthropologist or whether he is really a psychologist or a psychiatrist.

Certainly, the field of anthropology has been to some extent transformed by this very real interest and concern with the individual in the culture, and without trying to determine anything in the way of priority, it seems to me that Harry Stack Sullivan made a very real contribution, at the side of Sapir; certainly he played a very definite part in this important development.

A second interest of Sullivan's that I was privileged to observe at first hand, was his very real concern with problems of international relations. Shortly after I first joined UNESCO over three years ago, there was a meeting that was referred to in the corridors of UNESCO as "a meeting of wise men," in which eight social scientists from different countries came together to help those who were in charge of the "Tensions Project" to see some of the directions in which the work might go. Sullivan was a member of that group, and out of that meeting came a book edited by Hadley Cantril, *Tensions That Cause Wars.*

I still remember many of the contributions to that discussion. I remember that at the very end of the period as we were getting ready to leave, one of the members of the group, a Hungarian sociologist, said to Cantril, "How did you get these people together; in particular, how did you have the genius to invite Harry Stack Sullivan to this meeting?" What he meant was that Sullivan had a kind of stimulating, disturbing, and finally soothing and coordinating effect on the group. This came out clearly in Sullivan's actual part in the proceedings, and it was related to his very real understanding of the way in which the psychiatrist and the social scientist could be mutually helpful.

A third personal experience which also bears upon his view of the psychiatrist in relation to the social scientist came about at the time of the formation of the World Federation for Mental Health, also about three years ago. This new organization, which is now functioning effectively, and I hope will flourish even very actively in the future, was formed at an International Congress in London in the summer of 1948. Before that meeting, and this was directly as a result of Sullivan's suggestion, a group of about twenty social scientists from various countries got together to set up a kind of working paper, a statement for the World Federation of Mental Health. It was Harry Stack Sullivan who suggested holding this meeting in the first place, and his was the inspiration which resulted in bringing together these social scientists from a number of different countries and different backgrounds, to see what was meant by mental health in relation to world crisis.

Sullivan felt that this was not a job for the psychiatrist alone, the psychoanalyst alone, the social worker alone; there must be cooperation between psychiatrists and others. Sullivan himself worked hard to achieve that cooperation. At the actual meetings, when things seemed to be going badly, he went off for a day with three or four of his colleagues, a little distance away from the main group, and returned with a Preamble which he presented to the whole group; that was the beginning of the Statement that was finally issued on "Mental Health and World Citizenship."

I want to turn now to the three excellent papers that we have heard, and I want to state what a very real pleasure it was to listen to all three of them, and how much I learned from the detailed indications of Sullivan's thinking, and his relation to other social scientists. I am personally very proud to be a footnote to these three papers.

As I said earlier, I do not think there is much point in trying to establish priorities, in determining who made the first step in this or that direction. Dr. Cottrell will remember that at a very recent meeting of the Social Science Research Council in Skytop, Pennsylvania, we discussed the contributions of W. I. Thomas, and many of us found striking parallels between the thinking of W. I. Thomas and of Kurt Lewin, particularly in Thomas' stress on the "situation." Now we see further parallels between Lewin and Sullivan, and Moreno and Sullivan. As I say, we need not attempt to decide historically who got what from whom, and when, and under what condition, because it seems to me that the far more important thing is to make use of what we have, and to take advantage of a point of view that is of such fundamental importance in this whole field.

I would like, however, if there is time, to have Professor

Murphy say another word about the dichotomy of "past" and "present" in the thinking of Sullivan. My own interpretation of Sullivan is a little different. I had the feeling that Sullivan, perhaps a little more than Lewin, believed that understanding the present did require a careful analysis of the past. Certainly, he was very much aware of the problems of culture; and of how the individual was shaped by culture. To the extent that he looked into culture, he was really asking certain questions about previous experience. I suppose it could be said that if you make a study of the present, you must inevitably include the past, to the extent that it has determined the present. If that is so, then the whole argument turns out to be an argument about terms, and need not delay us much longer. Certainly, Sullivan was interested in etiology, even though, as Professor Murphy correctly pointed out, the final answer was not forthcoming. This very interest in etiology would seem to make it inevitable that Sullivan would be concerned with the previous history of the individual, before he came to the psychiatrist, before he reached the point at which he was. As I say, this may be a question of language.

As far as Sullivan's neglect of the effect of the overall social structure on the individual is concerned, I think probably that is largely true, but I do want to point out that toward the end of his life, Sullivan was very much interested in comparative national characteristics, and in the study of differences in the background of different national groups. Certainly *Psychiatry* as a journal opened its pages to students of national character more than did any other—certainly more than any other journal not directly devoted to this problem. One of the most recent numbers contained an article by Sullivan himself called "Towards a Psychiatry of Peoples." Sullivan, of course, used the word "psychiatry" to cover a rather broad range of interests. In this article there were suggestions made as to how we could go about finding out something more about the background of people of different nationalities, including something of the institutional and cultural and social factors that made people of different nationalities different. So, without for a moment denying the importance of the limitations which Dr. Murphy has indicated, I think that toward the end of his life, Sullivan was trying to attack some-what more directly this very important problem.

In the paper by Cottrell and Foote, in which seven various directions of future possible research are described, all of which seem to be to contain important promise of future activity, I would like to single out for just a few comments two or three points that struck me particularly.

I was a little dissatisfied, if Dr. Cottrell will forgive my saying so, with the reference to Sullivan's insistence on the permanence of early patterns of personality in shaping the whole future development of the individual. I believe that in some of his early writings, he says something to this effect, but certainly at a later date, he was one of those who, more than anyone else, insisted that there was no time in life when change could not take place, when something could not be added or subtracted, or when a new social setting or added therapy might not effect a marked change in personality. I remember (and this is taking unfair advantage of Dr. Cottrell) that in a portion of the Statement on "Mental Health and the World Situation," Sullivan was mainly responsible for a specific paragraph running something like this: "Of course, the early experiences are very important, but there is no time in life when change may not occur, no time in life when further learning is not possible." Here again we may be differing on a matter of semantics or semiotics, because it may be that when Cottrell and Foote speak of the permanence of early pat-terns according to Sullivan, and I speak of Sullivan's insistence on possible change, it may be that there are some changes that may occur and some characteristics that may be permanent. I do feel strongly, however, that Sullivan, in my own view of him, was not quite so narrow as to believe that what was determined in early infancy would necessarily remain unchanged through life.

As far as the effect of group therapy or group psychotherapy is concerned, I realize that Sullivan played very little part in the more recent developments in this area, but I wonder whether his own early study of schizophrenia was not one of the first direct contributions to the field of group psychotherapy. It may not have been labeled that, but if one were to write a complete history of group psychotherapy, one would have to include his study of the manner in which a new environment, where schizophrenics lived together and were treated together, had very significant therapeutic effect.

Just a word about the "pseudo-community" to which Dr. Cottrell made reference. This is not by way of criticism or addition, but it does seem to me that the term "pseudocommunity" can be applied to many normal reactions, and not just to the abnormal. Many of us act in certain ways because we think the people around us have certain beliefs or attitudes. I am thinking of something that came out at a recent meeting, where it was pointed out that many individuals would be much readier to make certain changes in race relationships except for their belief that a lot of other people wouldn't stand for those changes. Yet the majority of individuals in this group were willing. This is also a "pseudo-community," but it is not restricted to the psychotic patient. This represents a concept, which, I think, plays an important part in many groups that are presumably normal, or at least not psychotic.

A final question to Dr. Johnson. I was struck by Dr. Johnson's reference to "observing the observer." After our Roffey Park meeting, Dr. Sullivan invited a number of the participants to send in to the journal *Psychiatry* their comments on what had gone on; many of you have probably seen these articles. It was very interesting to see how differently the same phenomena, the behavior of the group, looked to the different participants. That came out clearly only when they wrote down their remarks and published them in *Psychiatry*. Here was an example of Sullivan's concrete effort to discover more about how the same social phenomena looked to a number of different people, all of them presumably intelligent and objective, and yet seeing different things in the same group presentation in which they all had participated.

I want to emphasize Dr. Johnson's remarks that Sullivan was looking toward a future possibility of doing research toward changing institutions to make group relations and international relations more successful and less hostile than they are.

Perhaps I may be permitted to add one final little anecdote that is somewhat personal, but it expresses my own reaction to my association to Dr. Sullivan. At one of the Roffey Park meetings, Dr. Sullivan got quite irritated at something that went on, and began to criticize rather violently a lot of the people present. Every comment that was made for a brief period of time evoked some irritable reaction on the part of Sullivan. Then the meeting was over and I saw him sitting all alone on a chair not very far away, so I went over and sat down near him. He said: "I guess I was pretty bad. I kept insulting everybody right and left." "Yes," said I, "you insulted me too." "Oh," he replied, "that is the least of my worries." I remember feeling very pleased and proud that he thought he couldn't insult me! We were too good friends for that to happen. That was the one "insult" that he didn't need to worry about.

It is true that he did irritate a lot of people. He stepped on people's toes, but these very same people almost always ended up by respecting, admiring and liking him.

I am very proud and happy to participate in a well deserved tribute to a great man.

DISCUSSION*

PATRICK MULLAHY

I SHOULD like to discuss one or two points which Drs. Murphy and Cattell have raised in their criticisms of Sullivan. They apparently believe that field theory *should* be able to "cope with present realities without our getting lost in the attempt at reconstruction of the past." They seem to agree with Lewin that field theory in psychology is and must be in the nature of the case an ahistorical science and they appear to think that Sullivan's conception of "eidetic people" lead to undesirable theoretical results.

Since they base their arguments ultimately on philosophical considerations, a brief examination of some of the philosophical issues involved seem to be in order.

While it is true that no two events are absolutely identical, a recognition of this fact does not dispose of every problem connected with the Heraclitean doctrine of a flux. For example, while change apparently occurs all the time, there are continuities (as well as discontinuities), recurrences, *kinds* of events and relative identities in nature. If nature really were a Heraclitean flux, I believe knowledge would not be possible.

The issue as to reconstruction of the past raises profound problems, both psychological and epistemological. This much we know: that there can be no understanding of the *present* without generalizations which are available because of past experience. As C. I. Lewis has observed, for credibility of the observation, " 'White paper' is now before me, I must have, in addition to the sense presentation, those generalizations which would not be available in the early experience of an infant, and which will

* I have revised the comments I made at the symposium.—P. M.

223

enable prediction, with a degree of assurance, of the corrobora-
tion in further experience of what the reality of white paper
before me would imply." [1] These generalizations are based on
memory.

However, such generalizations are available as remembered.
And, as such, they are not sufficient for *theoretical* purposes,
partly because remembering is not always trustworthy. A further generalization is needed "to the effect that when such data
of memory are given, the seemingly remembered experience
may, with some degree of credibility, be accepted as actual." [2]

Because these issues are fundamental and decisive for an
operationalist methodology, I want to pursue Lewis' argument
a bit further. (An appeal to a *faculty* of memory, of course, is
ruled out.) What basis have we for saying that the seemingly
remembered may, with some degree of credibility, be accepted?
Are we caught in a circular web of argument? Since a prag-
matist's case rests *ultimately* on appeal to the "epistemological
present," how can we ever validate a statement about what is
not present, of what is seemingly remembered?

In general terms, the answer lies with a congruence (not
a mere coherence) theory of memorial validation. Congruence
is defined thus: "*A set of statements, or a set of supposed facts
asserted, will be said to be congruent if and only if they are so
related that the antecedent probability of any one of them will
be increased if the remainder of the set can be assumed as given
premises.*" [3] It is to be noted that congruence involves a statement of probability—sometimes very high probability—not cer-
tainty.

Mystery stories exhibit the meaning of congruence. "Here
various items of evidence are given initially, or introduced as the
story unfolds; some as authenticated fact, and some having
greater or smaller initial credibility. Taken separately, these
afford small confirmation of the hypothesis which eventually
gives the solution, and may not even serve to suggest it. Also,
any single one of them is congruent with various alternative

[1] *An Analysis of Knowledge and Valuation*, p. 335.

[2] Op. cit., p. 336.

[3] Op. cit., p. 338.

hypotheses. But the picture-puzzle relation of these items, at one stroke raises what was merely conjecturable before to the status of the highly probable, when the last piece of evidence fits into place." [4]

In an analogous fashion a memory affirmation becomes probable. Something "I seem to remember as happening to me at the age of five may be of small credibility; but if a sufficient number of such seeming recollections hang together sufficiently well and are not incongruent with any other evidence, then it becomes highly probable that what I recollect is fact." [5]

Complete consistency is not enough. "There must be *direct* evidence of something which would be improbable coincidence on any other hypothesis than that which is corroborated— The indispensable item is some direct empirical datum;—the facts of our seeming to remember; and without that touchstone of presentation, relations of congruence would not advance us a step toward determination of the empirically actual or the validly credible." [6]

While there is much more to be said about these things, I want to mention another point regarding the argument about memory. It is this: without genuinely knowable past experience, we could have no knowledge of the empirical world, of ourselves, or of others. Genuinely to doubt our knowledge of the past wholesale would be to abandon or lose any criterion by which anything—including our own doubt—might be appraised or corroborated. It would mean, as Lewis has emphasized, that we would entirely erase the distinction between fact and phantasy.

Since Drs. Murphy and Cattell claim that field theory in psychology deals only with the present, I wish to emphasize that present observation leans on past experience for its credibility and for any assertion we make about the present. [7] Every

4 Op. cit., pp. 346-347.
5 Op. cit., p. 352.
6 Op. cit., pp. 352-353.
7 I do not deny of course that the validation of memory assertions involves practical difficulties, but I am concerned with the logic of this issue. Nor do I wish to deny that psychoanalysts have played fast and loose with many so-called memories of their patients.

statement of fact has a limiting reference to both past and future. In his more recent lectures, Sullivan has stressed this point regarding psychiatric inquiry. Dewey has stated the logic of this in his usual masterly fashion. He says: "No *mere* flux can be noted, appraised or estimated. A change is characterized in terms of direction—*from* something *to* something. 'The sun is rising'— that is, it was below the horizon, but is now moving further and further above the horizon. Such propositions as 'It is sweet or red' state . . . either that something is becoming or has become a changed quality, or else that it has the capacity to change —to redden or sweeten—something else." [8]

Moreover dating "depends upon connecting a particular occurrence with other events coming before and after in such a way that taken together they constitute a temporal series or history. If I say that 'I was home at five o'clock yesterday,' I am in fact constructing as an object of grounded belief a sequential course of events. 'Yesterday' has no significance save in connection with today, the day-before-yesterday and a series of tomorrows. 'Five o'clock' has no significance save in connection with four and six o'clock and so on." [9]

Sullivan's formulation of memory, recall and recollection as stated in his *Conceptions of Modern Psychiatry* asserts or implies (1) that human beings "fix" somewhere and somehow meaningful "records" or "traces" of everything they live through, that is, of the pattern of how the organism and significant environment existed at a given time in a situation, (2) that recall is the functional activity, or perduring manifestation of this organization of one's past, (3) that recall may or may not operate without conscious awareness, and (4) that we have or can have genuine knowledge of the past. Thus I cannot know anything about myself now except in relation to what I was and did this morning, last week, and last year, and also in relation to tomorrow or next week. A perduring sense of self depends on memory, if only because the latter furnishes continuity to experience.

[8] John Dewey, *Logic, The Theory of Inquiry,* Henry Holt & Co., New York, 1938, p. 221.

[9] John Dewey, op. cit., p. 225.

I turn to another aspect of the problem and role of memory. Drs. Murphy and Cattell find the phrase "remnant of the past" objectionable, claiming it to be synonymous with Freud's "reminiscences." Yet they are careful to say that the "teeming present" contains "heirlooms from the past." Now I shall not ask what an heirloom from the past, according to them, might mean. I shall assume that the phrase is as innocently meant as "remnant of the past" actually is. In any case, I wish to study briefly what Sullivan meant when he talked about the role of past experience in present behavior.

According to him, symbol processes represent the "enduring manifestations" of past experience. Since experience is cumulative and dynamic, symbol processes and personifications likewise undergo change and modification. To say that we "carry" these eidetic people around with us is assuredly a loose and metaphorical way of speaking. But so are such phrases as "carrying" ideas in our heads, etc. Yet unless such phrases are literally meant or applied, they are innocent. Is it necessary to dispense with such innocent use of metaphor? To speak of eidetic people operative in a situation is to specify or indicate in a shorthand phrase the way or one of the ways by which past interpersonal experiences has moulded, structured personality such that it is effective in, or has dynamic effects in, one's present and anticipated interpersonal relations. Symbol processes are acts or activities of the person, which have evolved from a long interpersonal history. As in the case of every other activity of the person, they occur as integral aspects of the total behavior of the person in a situation, and as such they are in some sense efficacious, like every aspect of the mental life of the person. For similar reasons symbol processes and personifications are or appear to be modified by new situations. This is a natural consequence of interpersonal relations.

For the psychiatrist, eidetic people may serve as clues to three things: (1) the way in which the patient integrates a situation with the therapist; (2) the way in which the patient's personality has been moulded by and has developed from past interpersonal experience; and (3) the patient's foresight or lack of it for integrating new and more satisfactory relationships. However,

I am not saying that such clues are sufficient in themselves for effective therapy. Certainly not. However, this example illustrates the fact that Sullivan's conception of eidetic people is no small matter.

When a person is brought or enabled to see—perhaps after a good deal of preliminary work—that some of his experiences, for example, as manifested by his integrations with eidetic people, are "distorted," and that these eidetic people, as aspects of his total behavior, function so as to *help* obstruct his interpersonal relations, making the latter more "complex" and frustrating, an important milestone in therapy is reached. While it would be absurd to say that eidetic people literally "interact" in situations, they represent important components or constitutive elements in a person's "maladjusted" or "neurotic" interpersonal relations.

If "eidetic people" were not in some way efficacious in human behavior—as indicated above—there would be no point, I think, in helping the patient become aware of them. Any insight into the origin and nature of these eidetic people would have no effect. In other words, such symbolic representations are, at least sometimes, and under certain conditions, strategic components of human behavior to "attack" in order to assist the patient in bringing about therapeutic change. Precisely because they do not exist as disembodied or as substantial entities, but as functional aspects of the total personality in interpersonal configurations, any change in them tends to help bring about change in total behavior and in personality make-up.

To the best of my knowledge, Sullivan would not accept any doctrines of "habit" or "set" or "conditional response," etc. He was in fact quite hostile to most or all of them. Apparently he did not believe that any formulation in terms of habits or sets or whatever could plausibly and adequately account for the complexity of human behavior as he encountered it, or adequately serve the needs of dynamic psychotherapy. For him, "dynamism," a configuration of energy which signifies only relatively enduring capacity to bring about change, was preferable.

In times of difficulty, memory is often the preserver of our personal integrity. For it reminds us of what we were or can be.

BIBLIOGRAPHY OF
HARRY STACK SULLIVAN

BIBLIOGRAPHY OF HARRY STACK SULLIVAN *

1924

"Schizophrenia: Its Conservative and Malignant Features." *Amer. J. Psychiatry,* 4:77-91.

1925

"The Oral Complex." *Psychoanalytic Rev.,* 12:31-38.
"Peculiarity of Thought in Schizophrenia." *Amer. J. Psychiatry,* 5:21-86.

1926

"Erogenous Maturation." *Psychoanalytic Rev.,* 13:1-15.
"Regression: A Consideration of Reversive Mental Processes." *State Hosp. Quart.,* 11:208-217, 387-394, and 651-668.
"The Importance of a Study of Symbols in Psychiatry." *Psyche* (London), 8:81-93.

1927

"Affective Experience in Early Schizophrenia." *Amer. J. Psychiatry,* 6:468-483.
"The Onset of Schizophrenia." *Amer. J. Psychiatry,* 7:105-134.
"Mental Hygiene and the Modern World." *Modern World,* 1:153-157.
"The Common Field of Research and Clinical Psychiatry." *Psychiatric Quart.,* 1:276-291.
Discussion. "The Narrowing of the Gap Between the Functional and the Organic" by William A. White. *Amer. J. Psychiatry,* 7:228-229.

* Grateful acknowledgment is due Mrs. Helen Perry, managing editor of *Psychiatry,* for preparing this bibliography.—The Editor.

1928

"Affective Experience in Early Schizophrenia." *Proc. Assoc. Research N. and M. Disease*, 5:141-158.

"Tentative Criteria of Malignancy in Schizophrenia." *Amer. J. Psychiatry*, 7:759-787.

Proceedings First Colloquium on Personality Investigation (with the American Psychiatric Association Committee on Relations with the Social Sciences), Baltimore, The Lord Baltimore Press, 102 pp.

"Medical Education—An Editorial Comment." *Amer. J. Psychiatry*, 7:837-839.

"Psychiatric Research—An Editorial Comment." *Amer. J. Psychiatry*, 7:1075-1077.

1929

"Research in Schizophrenia." *Amer. J. Psychiatry*, 9:553-567.

1930

Farewell Lectures; Sheppard and Enoch Pratt Hospital. Privately circulated.

"The Socio-genesis of Homosexual Behavior in Males (Abstract)." *Amer. Sociol. Soc. Papers*, 24:281-282.

Proceedings Second Colloquium on Personality Investigation (with the American Psychiatric Association Committee on Relations of Psychiatry and the Social Sciences and the Social Science Research Council), Baltimore, The Johns Hopkins Press, 206 pp.

"The Relation of Onset to Outcome in Schizophrenia." *Schizophrenia (Dementia Praecox)*; Baltimore, Williams and Wilkins, 10:111-118.

1931

"Environmental Factors and Course Under Treatment of Schizophrenia." *Med. J. and Rec.*, 133:19-22.

"Socio-Psychiatric Research: Its Implications for the Schizophrenia Problem and for Mental Hygiene." *Amer. J. Psychiatry*, 10:977-991.

"Training of the General Medical Student in Psychiatry." *Amer. J. Orthopsychiatry*, 10:519-540.

"Personality Differentials as Antecedents and Consequences of Acculturation." *Proceedings Hanover Conference Social Science Research Council.*

1932

Personal Psychopathology. Privately circulated.

1933

"Mental Disorders." *Encyclopedia of the Social Sciences*, 10:313-319.

"Psychoanalysis and Psychiatric Education." *Proceedings National Committee Mental Hygiene Conference on Psychiatric Education.*

1934

"Psychiatry." *Encyclopedia of the Social Sciences*, 12:578-580.

1935

"Psychiatric Training as a Prerequisite to Psychoanalytic Practice." *Amer. J. Psychiatry*, 91:1117-1126.

Abstracts of Discussion. *Proceedings National Research Council Conference on Personality and Culture.*

1936

Proceedings National Research Council Sub-Committee on Training Fellowships. Privately circulated.

1937

"A Note on the Implications of Psychiatry, the Study of Interpersonal Relations, for Investigations in the Social Sciences." *Amer. J. Sociol.*, 42:846-861.

"William Alanson White—1870-1937." *Amer. J. Psychiatry*, 93: 1480-1482.

1938

"Psychiatry: Introduction to the Study of Interpersonal Relations, I." *Psychiatry*, 1:121-134.

"The William Alanson White Psychiatric Foundation—an Editorial." *Psychiatry*, 1:135-140.

"The Washington School of Psychiatry—an Editorial." *Psychiatry*, 1:140-141.

"This Journal—an Editorial." *Psychiatry*, 1:141-143.

"Security of the American Commonwealths—an Editorial." *Psychiatry*, 1:419-420.

"Antisemitism—an Editorial." *Psychiatry*, 1:593-598.

1939

"Intuition, Reason and Faith—an Editorial." *Psychiatry*, 2:129-132.

"Psychiatry and the National Defense—an Editorial." *Psychiatry*, 2:133-135.

"Psychiatry and the National Defense." *U.S. Naval Med. Bull.*, 37:273-276.

"A Note on Formulating the Relationship of the Individual and the Group." *Amer. J. Sociol.*, 44:932-937.

"Edward Sapir, Ph.D., Sc.D., 1884-1939." *Psychiatry*, 2:159.

"The Support of Psychiatric Research and Teaching—an Editorial." *Psychiatry*, 2:273-279.

"Summary and Critique—A Formal Discussion of Physical and Cultural Environment in Relation to the Conservation of Mental Health." *Mental Health* (eds. Forest Ray Moulton and Paul O. Komoral); Lancaster, Pa., The Science Press, 1939 (470 pp.) in particular, pp. 276-278 of Chapter 5.

"Responsibility—an Editorial" (with Ernest E. Hadley and Thomas Harvey Gill). *Psychiatry*, 2:599-602.

1940

"Conceptions of Modern Psychiatry." The First William Alanson White Memorial Lectures. *Psychiatry*, 3:1-117.

"Memorandum on a Psychiatric Reconnaissance, and A Psychiatric Gloss on a Sociological Study." In *Studies of Negro Youth*: Amer. Council on Education, Youth Commission.

"National Solidarity: Bulletin from the William Alanson White Psychiatric Foundation to Psychiatrists and Other Physicians." *Psychiatry*, 3:326-327.

"The Eagle, the Lion, and the Giant Squid—an Editorial." *Psychiatry*, 3:437-441.

"Memorandum on the Utilization of Psychiatry in the Promotion of National Security" (from the William Alanson White Psychiatric Foundation). *Psychiatry*, 3:483-492.

"Psychiatry and the National Defense" (with a committee of the Southern Psychiatric Association). *Psychiatry*, 3:619-624.

"A Minimum Psychiatric Inspection of Registrants: William Alanson White Psychiatric Foundation Bulletin" (largely incorporated in U.S. Selective Service System Medical Bulletin Number One). *Psychiatry*, 3:625-627.

"Propaganda and Censorship: William Alanson White Psychiatric Foundation Memorandum." *Psychiatry*, 3:628-632.

1941

"Selective Service System Psychiatry—an Editorial." *Psychiatry*, 4:118-120.

"Psychiatry and the National Defense." *Psychiatry*, 4:201-217.

"A Seminar on Practical Psychiatric Diagnosis (for Selective Service System Psychiatrists)." *Psychiatry*, 4:265-283.

"Selective Service Psychiatry" (an extract from the President's annual report to the Board of Trustees of the William Alanson White Psychiatric Foundation). *Psychiatry*, 4:440-464.

"Psychiatry in the Emergency." *Mental Hygiene*, 25:5-10.

"Psychiatric Aspects of Morale." *Amer. J. Sociol.*, 47:277-301.

"Mental Hygiene and National Defense." In *Mental Health Bulletin of Illinois Society for Mental Hygiene*, March 1, 1941.

1942

"Completing Our Mobilization—an Editorial." *Psychiatry*, 5:263-282.

"Psychiatry, the Army, and the War" (an extract from the President's annual report to the Board of Trustees of the William Alanson White Psychiatric Foundation). *Psychiatry*, 5:435-442.

"A Year of Selective-Service Psychiatry." *Mental Hygiene*, 26:7-15.

"Whither? and How?—an Editorial." *Psychiatry*, 5:93-99.

1943

"How Sweet *Are* the Uses of Adversity—an Editorial." *Psychiatry*, 6:217-240.

1944

"Psychiatric State of the Nation" (an editorial including a memorandum by M. F. Ashley Montagu on *The Races of Mankind*). *Psychiatry*, 7:183-189.

"Can There be Peace?—an Editorial." *Psychiatry*, 7:425-426.

1945

"The Soldier's Return—an Editorial." *Psychiatry*, 8:111-112.

"For a National Mental Health Council—an Editorial." *Psychiatry*, 8:235-243.

1946

"The Cultural Revolution to End War—an Editorial on the Second William Alanson White Memorial Lectures by Major-General G. B. Chisholm." *Psychiatry*, 9:81-87. Published also in *The Psychiatry of Enduring Peace and Social Progress: The William Alanson White Memorial Lectures* by G. B. Chisholm, with a foreword by Abe Fortas and discussion by Henry A. Wallace, Watson B. Miller, Samuel W. Hamilton, and Ross McC. Chapman. Washington, William Alanson White Psychiatric Foundation.

1947

"Foreword" to the second printing of *Conceptions of Modern Psychiatry* (including a criticism of the theory by Patrick Mullahy). Washington, William Alanson White Psychiatric Foundation.

"Therapeutic Investigations in Schizophrenia." *Psychiatry*, 10:121.

"Notes on Investigation, Therapy, and Education in Psychiatry and Their Relations to Schizophrenia." *Psychiatry*, 10:271-280.

"Remobilization for Enduring Peace and Social Progress." *Psychiatry*, 10:239-252.
"The Study of Psychiatry. Three Orienting Lectures." *Psychiatry*, 10:355-371.
"Ten Years of Psychiatry, a Statement by the Editor." *Psychiatry*, 10:433-435.

1948

"The Meaning of Anxiety in Psychiatry and in Life." William Alanson White Memorial Award. *Psychiatry*, 11:1-13.
"Towards a Psychiatry of Peoples." *Psychiatry*, 11:105-116.
"Two International Conferences of Psychiatrists and Social Scientists." *Psychiatry*, 11:223-229.
"Psychiatry, Education, and the UNESCO 'Tensions Project'." *Psychiatry*, 11:371-375.
"The School and International Prospects—Address given at 1948 Convocation of Washington School of Psychiatry." *Psychiatry*, 11:xvii-xx.

1949

"Multidisciplined Coordination of Interpersonal Data" in *Culture and Personality*, edited by S. Stansfeld Sargent and Marian W. Smith, Viking Fund, 1949.

1950

"Tensions Interpersonal and International: A Psychiatrist's View" in *Tensions That Cause Wars*, edited by Hadley Cantril, University of Illinois Press, Urbana, Ill., 1950.

1951

'Psychiatric Aspects of Morale" in *Personality and Political Crisis*, edited by Alfred H. Stanton and Stewart E. Perry, The Free Press, Glencoe, Ill., 1951. Reprinted from *American Journal of Sociology*, 1941, but contains additional material.

Posthumously Edited Material

1949

"The Theory of Anxiety and the Nature of Psychotherapy." *Psychiatry,* 12:3-12.

"The Study of Psychiatry: 1948 Orienting Lectures." *Psychiatry,* 12:325-337.

1950

"The Illusion of Personal Individuality." *Psychiatry,* 13:317-332.

1951

"The Psychiatric Interview." *Psychiatry,* 14:361-373.